food insecurity:
when people must live with hunger
and fear starvation

The State of
2002
Food Insecurity in the World

About this report

This fourth edition of *The State of Food Insecurity in the World* (SOFI) provides the latest estimates of the number of chronically hungry people in the world and reports on global and national efforts to reach the goal set by the World Food Summit (WFS) in 1996 – to reduce that number to half the level reported at the time of the Summit by the year 2015.

The report is divided into four main sections. The first section, *Undernourishment around the world*, analyses the latest data on hunger. Other articles combine this data with other indicators to chart the fatal connection between hunger and mortality and the strategic connection between combating hunger and achieving the Millennium Development Goals.

The second section contains a special feature on mountain people and mountain environments. This presents preliminary results from a multidisciplinary study carried out as part of FAO's contribution to the International Year of Mountains. The study used newly available georeferenced data to estimate the number of mountain people vulnerable to food insecurity.

In the third section, *Towards the Summit commitments*, a series of articles discusses approaches to fulfilling the commitments in the WFS Plan of Action.

Finally, as in every edition of SOFI, two sets of tables provide detailed information on the prevalence in developing countries and countries in transition of undernourishment and on food availability, dietary diversification, poverty, health and child nutritional status.

SOFI draws on the ongoing work of FAO and its international partners in monitoring the nutritional status and analysing the vulnerability of populations worldwide. It represents part of FAO's contribution to the Inter-Agency Food Insecurity and Vulnerability Information and Mapping Systems initiative.

Food Insecurity and Vulnerability Information and Mapping Systems

I am very pleased to associate the Inter-Agency Working Group on FIVIMS (IAWG-FIVIMS) with this fourth edition of *The State of Food Insecurity in the World*. The information contained in this publication represents a substantial contribution to the objectives of FIVIMS, namely, to:

- increase global attention to problems of food insecurity;
- improve data quality and analysis through the development of new tools and capacity-building in developing countries;
- promote effective and better directed action aimed at reducing food insecurity and poverty;
- promote donor collaboration on food security information systems at the global and country levels;
- improve access to information through networking and sharing.

As the membership list indicates, the IAWG-FIVIMS represents diverse perspectives and interests. But we all share a commitment to reduce global food insecurity and vulnerability and to build sustainable livelihoods for the poor. Increasingly, the sustainable livelihood approach is seen as providing a framework for monitoring and assessing both food insecurity and vulnerability and the direction and impact of our efforts to alleviate them. Some examples of vulnerable livelihoods and vulnerable environments are detailed in SOFI, with a particular focus on mountain people in keeping with the designation of 2002 as the International Year of Mountains.

The international development environment in which IAWG-FIVIMS operates has changed markedly since the 1996 World Food Summit. The Millennium Development Goal (MDG) process has assumed a prominent role in development strategies and actions. The IAWG-FIVIMS looks forward to being fully involved with the MDG initiative and with efforts to monitor its implementation and impact at global and national levels.

As with previous issues of SOFI, IAWG members commend the FAO SOFI team for an excellent report on the state of food insecurity in the world.

Krishna Belbase (UNICEF)
Chair, IAWG-FIVIMS

IAWG-FIVIMS membership

Bilateral aid and technical agencies
Australian Agency for International Development (AusAID)
Canadian International Development Agency (CIDA)
European Commission (EC)
German Agency for Technical Cooperation (GTZ)
United States Agency for International Development (USAID)
United States Department of Agriculture (USDA)

United Nations and Bretton Woods agencies
Food and Agriculture Organization of the United Nations (FAO)
International Fund for Agricultural Development (IFAD)
International Labour Organization (ILO)
United Nations Department of Economic and Social Affairs (UNDESA)
Office for the Coordination of Humanitarian Affairs (OCHA)
United Nations Development Programme (UNDP)
United Nations Environment Programme (UNEP)
United Nations Children's Fund (UNICEF)
United Nations Population Fund (UNFPA)
World Bank (WB)
World Food Programme (WFP)
World Health Organization (WHO)
World Meteorological Organization (WMO)
United Nations System Standing Committee on Nutrition (UNS/SCN)
Consultative Group on International Agricultural Research (CGIAR)
International Food Policy Research Institute (IFPRI)
International Service for National Agricultural Research (ISNAR)
International Centre for Tropical Agriculture (CIAT)

International non-governmental organizations
Helen Keller International (HKI)
Save the Children Fund (SCF)
World Resources Institute (WRI)

Regional organizations
Southern African Development Community (SADC)
Permanent Interstate Committee for Drought Control in the Sahel (CILSS)

Contents

Foreword

Towards the World Food Summit target

TO PUT IT BLUNTLY, the state of food security in the world is not good. In each of the three previous editions of this report, the basic message has been essentially the same. Each year, we have reported a mixture of good news and bad news. The good news has been that the number of undernourished people in the developing world continues to decline. The bad news has been that the decline has been too slow, that our progress has been falling far short of the pace needed to reduce the number of hungry people by half by the year 2015 – the goal set at the World Food Summit (WFS) in 1996 and echoed in the Millennium Development Goals.

This year we must report that progress has virtually ground to a halt. Our latest estimates, based on data from the years 1998–2000, put the number of undernourished people in the world at 840 million, of whom 799 million live in developing countries. That figure represents a decrease of barely 2.5 million per year over the eight years since 1990–92, the period used as the starting point for the drive launched at the World Food Summit.

If we continue at the current pace, we will reach the WFS goal more than 100 years late, closer to the year 2150 than to the year 2015. Clearly, that is simply unacceptable.

To put it another way, in order to make up for the lagging progress to date and reach the World Food Summit goal on time, we must now strive to reduce the number of hungry people by 24 million each year from now until 2015, almost

66 We do not have the excuse that we cannot grow enough or that we do not know enough about how to eliminate hunger. 99

exactly ten times the pace achieved over the past eight years. That is simply imperative.

Daunting as the task may sound, achieving this accelerated rate of progress is also eminently possible. Quite frankly, the question is not whether we can afford to invest the resources, the energy, and the political commitment required to fight hunger. Rather, we must ask whether we can afford not to do so. The answer is that we cannot.

The price we pay for this lack of progress is heavy indeed. The hungry themselves pay most immediately and most painfully. But the costs are also crippling for their communities, their countries and the global village that we all inhabit and share.

Articles in this report document the crushing cost that hunger inflicts on the millions of people who experience it, measured in stunted physical and mental development, constricted opportunities, blighted health, shortened life expectancy, premature death. To cite just one example, every year, 6 million children under the age of five die as a result of hunger and malnutrition. That is roughly equivalent to the entire population of children under five in Japan, or in France and Italy combined.

Other articles in this report demonstrate that the reduced productivity, truncated working lives and suffocated opportunities of 799 million hungry people in the developing world hamstring economic progress and fuel environmental degradation and conflict at the national and international levels.

Clearly, the cost of inaction is prohibitive. Fortunately, the cost of progress is both calculable and affordable. The currency most urgently needed is not dollars but commitment.

At a side event of the World Food Summit: *five years later,* in June 2002, the FAO Secretariat presented a draft outline for an Anti-Hunger Programme, a strategic, cost-effective framework for national and international action to reduce

66 The cost of inaction is prohibitive. The cost of progress is both calculable and affordable. 99

hunger through agricultural and rural development and wider access to food.

According to this proposal, public investment of US$24 billion a year would be enough to jump-start an accelerated campaign against hunger that could reach the WFS goal. Taken in perspective, the price tag is startlingly low, dwarfed by the more than US$300 billion that the OECD nations transferred to support their own agriculture in 2001. As the economist Jeffrey Sachs has pointed out, in comparison to a global economy measured in the trillions, US$24 billion could be considered a "rounding error", representing barely five cents for every US$100 of income.

And the payoff would be impressively high. FAO has estimated that achieving the WFS goal would yield at least US$120 billion per year in benefits as a result of longer, healthier and more productive lives for several hundred million people freed from hunger.

The cost of the programme would be widely shared. Of various conceivable options, the Anti-Hunger Programme assumes that the costs would be shared equally, 50-50, between the international donor community and the developing countries themselves. On average, across all developing regions, this would require a 20 percent increase in developing countries' budgets for agricultural and rural development. For the developed countries and international financing institutions, it would represent a doubling of concessional funding to agricultural and rural development. This would restore official development assistance to the level before a steep decline in the 1990s that hit hardest in precisely those countries

Number of undernourished in the developing world: observed and projected ranges compared with the World Food Summit target

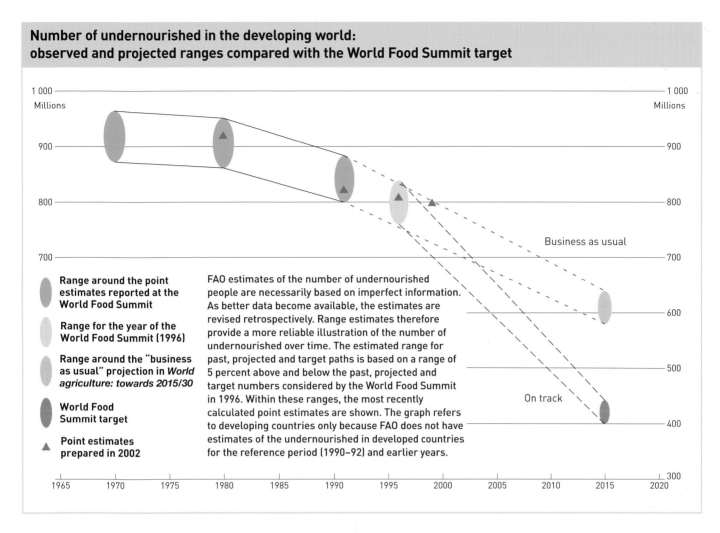

Range around the point estimates reported at the World Food Summit

Range for the year of the World Food Summit (1996)

Range around the "business as usual" projection in *World agriculture: towards 2015/30*

World Food Summit target

▲ **Point estimates prepared in 2002**

FAO estimates of the number of undernourished people are necessarily based on imperfect information. As better data become available, the estimates are revised retrospectively. Range estimates therefore provide a more reliable illustration of the number of undernourished over time. The estimated range for past, projected and target paths is based on a range of 5 percent above and below the past, projected and target numbers considered by the World Food Summit in 1996. Within these ranges, the most recently calculated point estimates are shown. The graph refers to developing countries only because FAO does not have estimates of the undernourished in developed countries for the reference period (1990–92) and earlier years.

where hunger is most widespread, as documented in this report.

And what would this investment buy? The Anti-Hunger Programme outlines a twin-track approach to reduce the number of hungry people rapidly and sustainably. It would provide access to food and deliver immediate relief to those most desperately in need, more than 200 million hard-core hungry people. And it would channel investment into sustainable agriculture and rural development, elevating productivity, incomes and hope in the rural areas in the developing world where more than three-quarters of the world's poor and hungry people live. The proposal also suggests key elements of a policy framework that would maximize the impact of these investments by inducing complementary flows of private investment and enabling the poor and hungry to realize their full development potential.

We do not have the excuse that we

cannot grow enough or that we do not know enough about how to eliminate hunger. What remains to be proven is that we care enough, that our expressions of concern in international fora are more than rhetoric, that we will no longer accept and ignore the suffering of 840 million hungry people in the world or the daily death toll of 25 000 victims of hunger and poverty.

We already produce more than enough food to provide an adequate diet for everyone. The Plan of Action of the 1996 World Food Summit set out clearly what needs to be done. The Anti-Hunger Programme suggests practical, affordable measures for translating the Plan of Action's sound concepts and worthy principles into immediate, effective action.

There can be no excuse for further delay. Hunger can be defeated. But only if we demonstrate our commitment by mobilizing a concerted and adequately financed campaign. Governments, the

international community, civil society and non-governmental organizations and the private sector have to work together, as an international alliance against hunger, to ensure that all people enjoy the most fundamental of human rights – the right to food that is essential to their very survival and existence.

Jacques Diouf
FAO Director-General

Undernourishment around the world

Hunger and mortality

MILLIONS OF PEOPLE, including 6 million children under the age of five, die each year as a result of hunger. Of these millions, relatively few are the victims of famines that attract headlines, video crews and emergency aid. Far more die unnoticed, killed by the effects of chronic hunger and malnutrition, a "covert famine" that stunts their development, saps their strength and cripples their immune systems.

Where prevalence of hunger is high, mortality rates for infants and children under five are also high, and life expectancy is low (see map and graphs). In the worst affected countries, a newborn child can look forward to an average of barely 38 years of healthy life (compared to over 70 years of life in "full health" in 24 wealthy nations). One in seven children born in the countries where hunger is most common will die before reaching the age of five.

Not all of these shortened lives can be attributed to the effects of hunger, of course. Many other factors combine with hunger and malnutrition to sentence tens of millions of people to an early death. The HIV/AIDS pandemic, which is ravaging many of the same countries where hunger is most widespread, has reduced average life expectancy across all of sub-Saharan Africa by nearly five years for women and 2.5 years for men.

Even after compensating for the impact of HIV/AIDS and other factors, however, the correlation between chronic hunger and higher mortality rates remains striking. Numerous studies suggest that it is far from coincidental. Since the early 1990s, a series of analyses have confirmed that between 50 and 60 percent of all childhood deaths in the developing world are caused either directly or indirectly by hunger and malnutrition.

Relatively few of those deaths are the result of starvation. Most are caused by a persistent lack of adequate food intake and essential nutrients that leaves children weak, underweight and vulnerable.

As might be expected, the vast majority of the 153 million underweight children under five in the developing world are concentrated in countries where the prevalence of undernourishment is high (see graph on facing page).

Even mild-to-moderate malnutrition greatly increases the risk of children dying from common childhood diseases. Overall, analysis shows that the risk of death is 2.5 times higher for children with only mild malnutrition than it is for children who are adequately nourished. And the risk increases sharply along with the severity of malnutrition (as measured by their weight-to-age ratio). The risk of death is 4.6 times higher for children suffering from moderate malnutrition and 8.4 times higher for the severely malnourished.

Common diseases often fatal for malnourished children

Infectious diseases are the immediate cause of death for most of the 11 million children under the age of five who die each year in the developing world. But the risk of dying from those diseases is far greater for children who are hungry and malnourished.

The four biggest killers of children are diarrhoea, acute respiratory illness, malaria and measles. Taken together, these four diseases account for almost half of all deaths among children under the age of five. Analysis of data from hospitals and villages shows that all four of these diseases are far more deadly to children who are stunted or underweight.

In the case of diarrhoea, numerous studies show that the risk of death is as much as nine times higher for children who are significantly underweight, the most common indicator of chronic undernutrition. Similarly, underweight children are two to three times more likely to die of malaria and acute respiratory infections, including pneumonia, than well-nourished children.

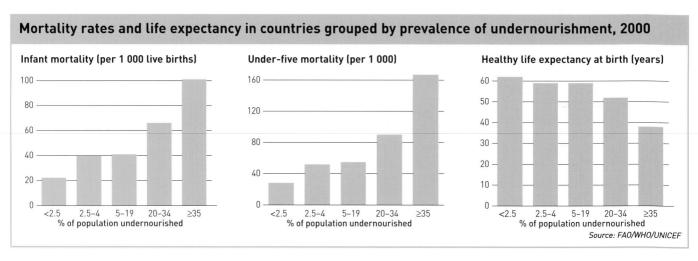

Mortality rates and life expectancy in countries grouped by prevalence of undernourishment, 2000

Source: FAO/WHO/UNICEF

Lack of dietary diversity and essential minerals and vitamins also contributes to increased child and adult mortality. Iron deficiency anaemia greatly increases the risk of death from malaria, and vitamin A deficiency impairs the immune system, increasing the annual death toll from measles and other diseases by an estimated 1.3–2.5 million children (see graph page 24).

Improving nutrition to save lives

The weight of evidence clearly argues that eliminating hunger and malnutrition could save millions of lives each year. That conclusion has been confirmed by a study that examined factors that had helped reduce child mortality during the 1990s. Topping the list were the decline in the proportion of children who were malnourished and lacking access to adequate water, sanitation and housing.

Correspondence between high rates of chronic hunger and childhood mortality, 2000

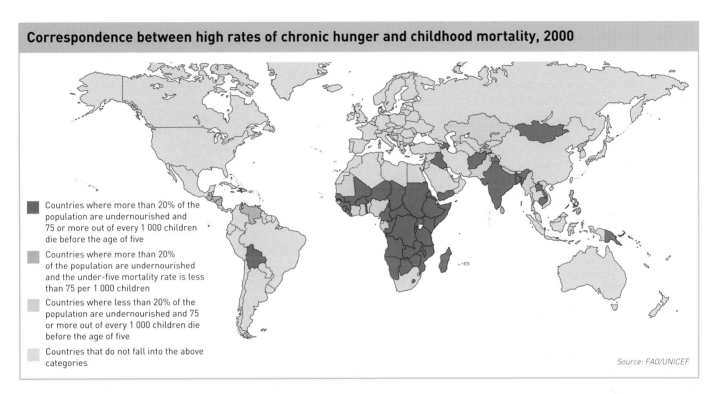

Countries where more than 20% of the population are undernourished and 75 or more out of every 1 000 children die before the age of five

Countries where more than 20% of the population are undernourished and the under-five mortality rate is less than 75 per 1 000 children

Countries where less than 20% of the population are undernourished and 75 or more out of every 1 000 children die before the age of five

Countries that do not fall into the above categories

Source: FAO/UNICEF

Hunger and child mortality

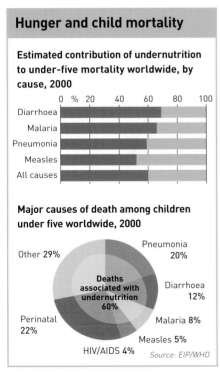

Estimated contribution of undernutrition to under-five mortality worldwide, by cause, 2000

Major causes of death among children under five worldwide, 2000

Other 29%
Pneumonia 20%
Deaths associated with undernutrition 60%
Diarrhoea 12%
Perinatal 22%
Malaria 8%
Measles 5%
HIV/AIDS 4%

Source: EIP/WHO

Proportion and number of underweight children, 1997–99

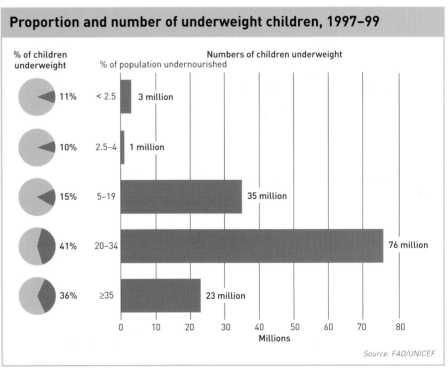

Source: FAO/UNICEF

Undernourishment around the world

Counting the hungry: latest estimates

FAO'S LATEST ESTIMATES of the number of undernourished people confirm an alarming trend – progress in reducing hunger in the developing world has slowed to a crawl and in most regions the number of undernourished people is actually growing.

Worldwide, the latest estimates indicate that 840 million people were undernourished in 1998–2000. This figure includes 11 million in the industrialized countries, 30 million in countries in transition and 799 million in the developing world. The latest figure of 799 million for the developing countries represents a decrease of just 20 million since 1990–92, the benchmark period used at the World Food Summit (WFS). This means that the average annual decrease since the Summit has been only 2.5 million, far below the level required to reach the WFS goal of halving the number of undernourished people by 2015. It also means that progress would now have to be accelerated to 24 million per year, almost 10 times the current pace, in order to reach that goal.

Closer examination reveals that the situation in most of the developing world is even bleaker than it appears at first glance. The marginal global gains are the result of rapid progress in a few large countries. China alone has reduced the number of undernourished people by 74 million since 1990–92. Indonesia, Viet Nam, Thailand, Nigeria, Ghana and Peru

have all achieved reductions of more than 3 million, helping to offset an increase of 96 million in 47 countries where progress has stalled. But if China and these six countries are set aside, the number of undernourished people in the rest of the developing world has increased by over 80 million since the WFS benchmark period.

When the number of undernourished is considered as a proportion of a country's total population, the picture is somewhat more encouraging. In the majority of developing countries, the proportion has actually decreased since the WFS. In

26 of the 61 developing countries that achieved a proportional decrease in undernourishment, however, the absolute number of undernourished people has continued to rise as a result of rapid population growth. One of those 26 countries is India, where the ranks of the undernourished have swollen by 18 million, despite the fact that the proportion fell from 25 to 24 percent.

Sub-Saharan Africa continues to have the highest prevalence of undernourishment and also has the largest increase in the number of undernourished

Proportions of undernourished in developing countries, 1990–92 and 1998–2000

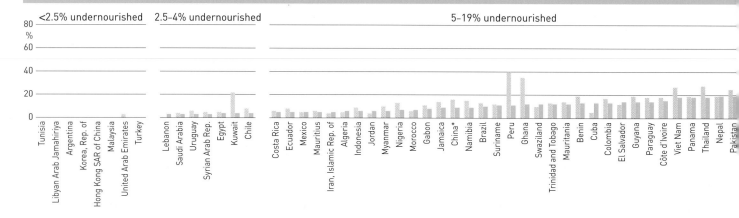

people. But the situation in Africa is not uniformly grim. Most of the increase took place in Central Africa, driven by the collapse into chronic warfare of a single country, the Democratic Republic of the Congo, where the number of undernourished people has tripled.

West Africa, with Southeast Asia and South America, has reduced significantly both the prevalence and the number of undernourished people. But prospects are troubling for Central America, the Near East and East Asia (excluding China), where both of these elements have increased.

Undernourished, 1998–2000 (millions)

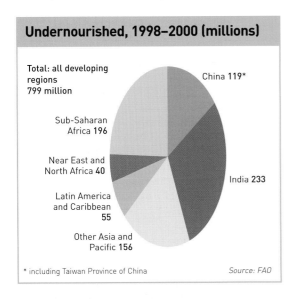

Total: all developing regions 799 million

China 119*
India 233
Other Asia and Pacific 156
Latin America and Caribbean 55
Near East and North Africa 40
Sub-Saharan Africa 196

* including Taiwan Province of China   *Source: FAO*

Number and proportion of undernourished, 1998–2000

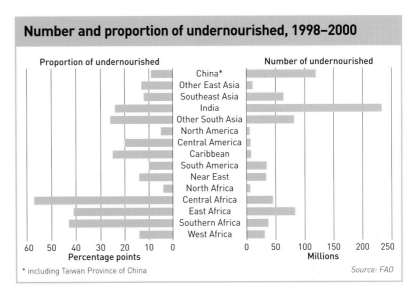

Proportion of undernourished   Number of undernourished

China*
Other East Asia
Southeast Asia
India
Other South Asia
North America
Central America
Caribbean
South America
Near East
North Africa
Central Africa
East Africa
Southern Africa
West Africa

60 50 40 30 20 10 0   0 50 100 150 200 250
Percentage points   Millions

* including Taiwan Province of China   *Source: FAO*

Towards the WFS goal at country level

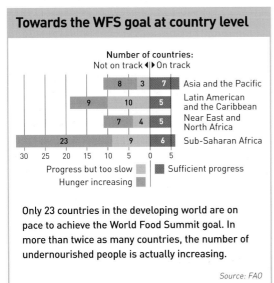

Number of countries:
Not on track ◀▶ On track

8	3	7	Asia and the Pacific
9	10	5	Latin American and the Caribbean
7	4	5	Near East and North Africa
23	9	6	Sub-Saharan Africa

30 25 20 15 10 5 0 5

Progress but too slow   Sufficient progress
Hunger increasing

Only 23 countries in the developing world are on pace to achieve the World Food Summit goal. In more than twice as many countries, the number of undernourished people is actually increasing.

Source: FAO

Change in undernourishment, 1990–92 to 1998–2000

Change in proportion of undernourished   Change in number of undernourished

China
Southeast Asia
South America
West Africa
Oceania
Caribbean
North Africa
North America
Central America
Southern Africa
Other East Asia
Other South Asia
East Africa
Near East
India
Central Africa

–10 –5 0 5 10 15 20   –70 –60 –50 –40 –30 –20 –10 0 10 20
Percentage points   Millions

Reduction (progress)   Increase (setback)

* including Taiwan Province of China   *Source: FAO*

Grey bars: 1990–92   Coloured bars: 1998–2000

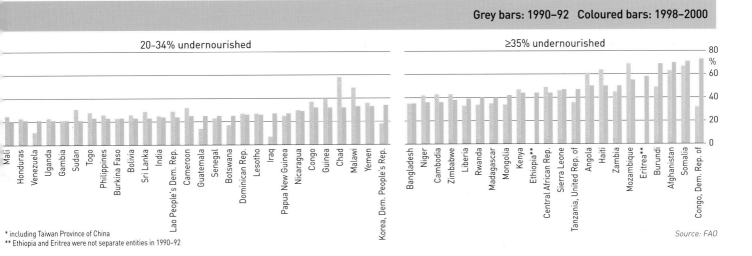

20–34% undernourished

Mali, Honduras, Venezuela, Uganda, Gambia, Sudan, Togo, Philippines, Burkina Faso, Bolivia, Sri Lanka, India, Lao People's Dem. Rep., Cameroon, Guatemala, Senegal, Botswana, Dominican Rep., Lesotho, Iraq, Papua New Guinea, Nicaragua, Congo, Guinea, Chad, Malawi, Yemen, Korea, Dem. People's Rep.

≥35% undernourished

Bangladesh, Niger, Cambodia, Zimbabwe, Liberia, Rwanda, Madagascar, Mongolia, Kenya, Ethiopia**, Central African Rep., Sierra Leone, Tanzania, United Rep. of, Angola, Haiti, Zambia, Mozambique, Eritrea**, Burundi, Afghanistan, Somalia, Congo, Dem. Rep. of

80 %
60
40
20
0

* including Taiwan Province of China
** Ethiopia and Eritrea were not separate entities in 1990–92

Source: FAO

Undernourishment around the world

Undernourishment, poverty and development

THE WORLD FOOD SUMMIT (WFS) in 1996 set the goal – to reduce the number of hungry people in the world by half before the year 2015. Four years later, that goal was echoed in the first of the Millennium Development Goals (MDGs), which set targets of reducing by half both the proportion of people who suffer from hunger and the proportion living on less than US$1 per day.

These targets are closely related; neither can be achieved without the other, and achieving both is essential to success in reaching the rest of the MDGs.

Poverty and hunger – mutual causes, devastating effects

Measures of food deprivation, nutrition and poverty are strongly correlated (see graphs). Countries with a high prevalence of undernourishment also have high prevalences of stunted and underweight children. In these countries, a high percentage of the population lives in conditions of extreme poverty. In countries where a high proportion of the population is undernourished, a comparably high proportion struggles to survive on less than US$1 per day.

While poverty is undoubtedly a cause of hunger, hunger can also be a cause of poverty. Hunger often deprives impoverished people of the one valuable resource they can call their own: the strength and skill to work productively. Numerous studies have confirmed that hunger seriously impairs the ability of the poor to develop their skills and reduces the productivity of their labour.

Hunger in childhood impairs mental and physical growth, crippling the capacity to learn and earn. Evidence from household food surveys in developing countries shows that adults with smaller and slighter body frames caused by undernourishment earn lower wages in jobs involving physical labour. Other studies have found that a 1 percent increase in the Body Mass Index (BMI, a measure of weight for a given height) is associated with an increase of more than 2 percent in wages for those toward the lower end of the BMI range.

Micronutrient deficiencies can also reduce work capacity (see pages 24–25). Surveys suggest that iron deficiency anaemia reduces productivity of manual labourers by up to 17 percent. As a result, hungry and malnourished adults earn lower wages. And they are frequently unable to work as many hours or years as well-nourished people, as they fall sick more often and have shorter life spans.

Hunger and the poverty of nations

Widespread hunger and malnutrition impair economic performance not only of individuals and families, but of nations. Anaemia alone has been found to reduce GDP by 0.5–1.8 percent in several countries (see graph). Studies in India, Pakistan, Bangladesh and Viet Nam estimated conservatively that the combined effect of stunting, iodine deficiency and iron deficiency reduced GDP by 2 to 4 percent. Recent calculations by FAO suggest that achieving the WFS goal of reducing the number of undernourished people by half by the year 2015 would yield a value of more than US$120 billion. That figure reflects the economic impact of longer, healthier, more productive lives for several hundred million people freed from hunger.

Nobel Prize-winning economist Robert Fogel has pointed out that hungry people cannot work their way out of poverty. He estimates that 20 percent of the population in England and France was effectively excluded from the labour force around 1790 because they were too weak and hungry to work. Improved nutrition, he calculates, accounted for about half of the economic growth in Britain and France between 1790 and 1880. Since many

---

Undernourishment, poverty and indicators for other Millennium Development Goals: 1995–2000

Undernourishment and poverty

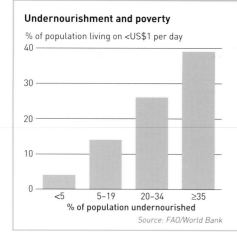

% of population living on <US$1 per day

% of population undernourished

Source: FAO/World Bank

Undernourishment and stunting

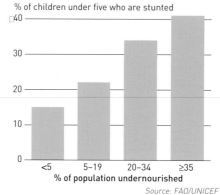

% of children under five who are stunted

% of population undernourished

Source: FAO/UNICEF

Undernourishment and female schooling

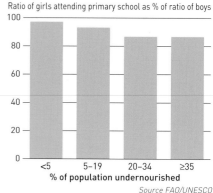

Ratio of girls attending primary school as % of ratio of boys

% of population undernourished

Source FAO/UNESCO

developing countries are as poor as Britain and France were in 1790, his analysis suggests reducing hunger could have a similar impact in developing countries today.

A key to Millennium Development Goals

Evidence clearly shows that failure to eliminate hunger will undermine efforts to reach the other MDGs as well (see box).

Hopes for achieving universal primary education and literacy, for example, will be thwarted while millions of hungry children suffer from diminished learning capacity or are forced to work instead of attending school. Low birth weight, protein energy malnutrition, iron deficiency anaemia and iodine deficiency are all linked to cognitive deficiencies. Hunger also limits school attendance. In Pakistan, a relatively small improvement in height for age increased school enrolment rates substantially: 2 percent for boys, 10 percent for girls. This steep increase for girls suggests one way in which reducing hunger would also accelerate another of the MDGs – promoting gender equality.

Data and analysis confirm that reducing hunger and malnutrition could have a decisive impact on reducing child mortality (see pages 6–7), improving maternal health (see pages 24–25), and on combating HIV/AIDS, malaria and other diseases (see pages 24–25).

Hunger impacts other Millennium Development Goals

Goal	Selected indicators	Impact of hunger
Achieve universal primary education	• net enrolment ratio • literacy rate	• reduces school attendance • impairs cognitive capacity
Promote gender equality	• ratio of girls to boys in primary education	• may reduce school attendance more for girls
Reduce child mortality	• under-five mortality rate	• associated with 60 percent of child deaths
Improve maternal health	• maternal mortality rate	• greatly increases risk of maternal death
Combat HIV/AIDS, malaria and other diseases	• HIV prevalence among pregnant women • death rates associated with malaria	• spurs migratory labour that increases spread of HIV • multiplies child death rates from two- to three-fold
Ensure environmental sustainability	• proportion of land area covered by forest	• leads to unsustainable use of forest lands and resources

Estimated cost of anaemia

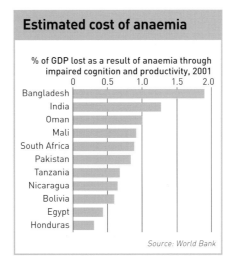

% of GDP lost as a result of anaemia through impaired cognition and productivity, 2001

Source: World Bank

Undernourishment and poverty

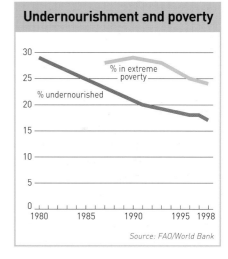

Source: FAO/World Bank

Undernourishment and maternal mortality

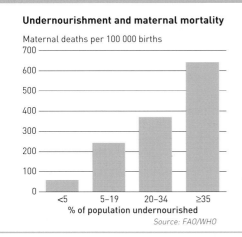

Source: FAO/WHO

Undernourishment and literacy

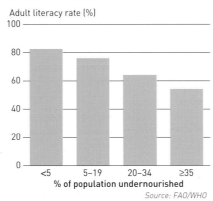

Source: FAO/WHO

Undernourishment and improved water

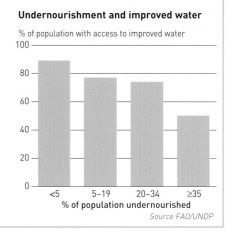

Source FAO/UNDP

Undernourishment around the world

Hunger hotspots

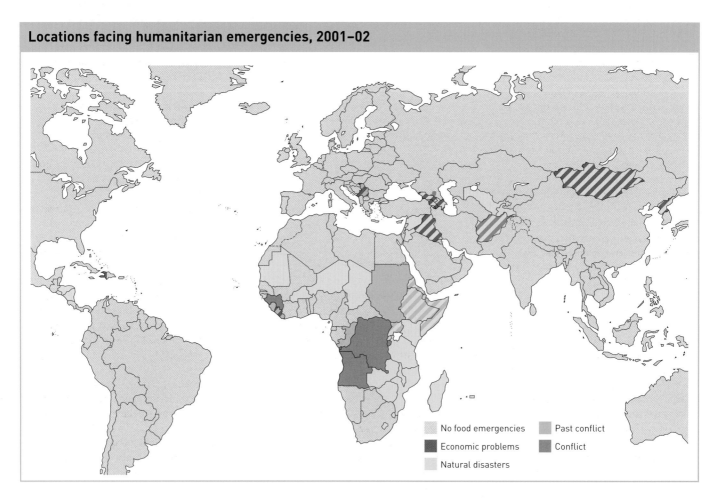

Locations facing humanitarian emergencies, 2001–02

No food emergencies
Economic problems
Natural disasters
Past conflict
Conflict

MOST OF THE WIDESPREAD HUNGER in a world of plenty results from grinding, deeply rooted poverty. In any given year, however, between 5 and 10 percent of the total can be traced to specific events: droughts or floods, armed conflict, political, social and economic disruptions. Frequently, these shocks strike countries already suffering from endemic poverty and struggling to recover from earlier natural and human-caused disasters. The past year was no exception.

As this report was being completed in June 2002, 32 countries faced exceptional food emergencies, with an estimated 67 million people requiring emergency food aid as a result. Both the number of countries and the number of people affected remained almost identical to a year earlier, as did the causes and

locations of many of them. As in previous years, drought and conflict were the most common causes and Africa the most affected region.

Worldwide, drought and other unfavourable weather conditions triggered food shortages in 21 of the 32 countries facing emergencies. War, civil strife and the lingering effects of past conflicts sparked crises in 15 countries, including several also plagued by bad weather. General economic problems severely undermined food security in eight countries, frequently in combination with adverse weather.

Dry weather and excessive rains during the growing season devastated food crops in several countries in southern Africa for the second consecutive year (see story, next page). In addition, the effects of ongoing and past civil conflicts threaten

the food security of over 14 million people in 11 African countries.

Asia received the most World Food Programme emergency food aid in 2001, mainly because of continuing crisis in the Democratic People's Republic of Korea. Eight other Asian countries faced food shortages resulting from droughts and severe winter weather, compounded by economic decline in many countries of the Commonwealth of Independent States.

In Afghanistan, decades of civil strife and a series of droughts have exposed millions of people to extreme hardship (see story, next page).

In Central America, a severe drought that devastated crops in 2001, combined with a collapse in world coffee prices, left families in rural areas in several countries of the region dependent on food aid.

13 million people face food emergency in southern Africa

Southern Africa faces its worst food crisis since the devastating drought of 1992. Nearly 13 million people in the subregion require emergency food aid, after a combination of droughts, floods and economic dislocations reduced harvests in several countries to half their normal levels or lower.

Worst affected has been Zimbabwe, where an estimated 6 million people need emergency food aid. Until recently, Zimbabwe has been an exporter of maize. But over the past two years, bad weather, political conflict and economic problems have combined to cripple production and impede imports. Ongoing disputes over land redistribution have led to severely reduced plantings in the commercial sector. Maize output has plummeted to less than one-quarter of the level achieved just two years earlier. The country faces an unprecedented deficit of more than 70 percent of its cereal requirements, at a time when it has little foreign exchange to import food.

Maize production has also fallen sharply in several other countries of the region. After the first year of bad harvests in 2001, average prices spiked higher by 150 percent in Zambia, 300 percent in Zimbabwe and almost 400 percent in Malawi, seriously undermining access to food for large sections of the population.

Total maize import requirements in nine countries in southern Africa have been estimated at about 3.4 million tonnes. Of those, some 1.2 million tonnes are needed as emergency food aid for the most vulnerable groups. Many families have already exhausted their coping

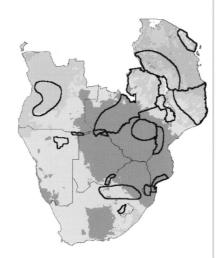

○ Maize-growing area

● Drought-affected area: rainfall < 70% normal, January–March 2002

Source: FAO

mechanisms after the poor harvest of 2001. In some areas, farmers did not gather any crop at all in 2002 and were eating tree stems and wild food at harvest time.

A major international effort has been launched to provide both relief food and seeds and other agricultural inputs for the next main planting season. The effort has been slow to get under way, however. As this report goes to press (end August 2002), only 25.5 percent of the joint WFP/FAO emergency appeal of US$507.3 million has been pledged, and some already donated food (maize) has been rejected by one recipient country for being genetically modified.

Maize requirements in southern Africa, 2000/01 to 2002/03

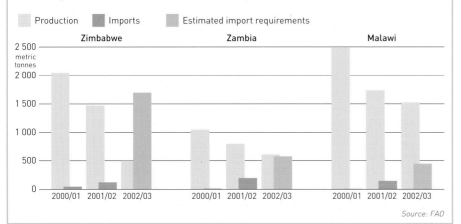

Source: FAO

Afghan drought and conflict

Even before the events of 11 September 2001, Afghanistan was gripped by a serious food crisis. After a third year of drought, cereal output in 2001 fell to barely half the production in 1998. Livestock herds, which are critical to the country's economy and food security, had been reduced by an estimated 40 percent.

Requirements for food imports for 2001–02 reached a record level of 2.2 million tonnes, but commercial imports dropped sharply when warfare erupted. Food aid increased but not enough to meet the needs of almost 10 million people, entirely dependent on food assistance.

Hunger and malnutrition have increased sharply in a country where stunting of children was reported to be as high as 52 percent in 1998, even before drought set in and food production plummeted.

Cereal production has rebounded significantly in 2002, buoyed by increased rainfall and better access to agricultural inputs. Output is expected to surpass the poor levels of the past three years, although still falling short of the 1998 harvest.

Despite this recovery, millions of people remain in need of food assistance. After years of conflict and drought, many families have exhausted their assets, have suffered deaths and disabilities or have been driven from their homes. Many of the country's irrigation systems lie in ruins and about half of the irrigated area has gone out of use. Large-scale investment is urgently needed to repair rural infrastructure and restore crop and livestock production.

Afghanistan cereal production

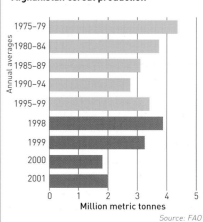

Source: FAO

Special feature

The vulnerability of mountain environments and mountain people

THIRTEEN PERCENT of the nearly 5 billion people in the developing world and Commonwealth of Independent States (CIS) live in mountain areas, many of which are isolated and environmentally fragile. Overcrowding has increased pressure on resources, leading to migration to cities and lowlands, erosion of traditional livelihood systems and greater food insecurity among those who remain.

A multidisciplinary FAO study, undertaken as a contribution to the International Year of Mountains, used newly available georeferenced data and maps to produce detailed information on the numbers, location, livelihoods and vulnerability of mountain people.

Mountain environments

The World Conservation Monitoring Centre (UNEP-WCMC) has defined six classes of mountains, together covering about 22 percent of the Earth's surface. Areas with an altitude of 2 500 metres or higher are always classified as mountains. Between 300 and 2 500 metres, areas are considered mountainous if they exhibit steep slopes or have a wide range of elevation in a small area (local elevation range or LER) or both. Many highland valleys and plateaus below 2 500 metres that lack slope and/or local elevation range are not classified as mountains.

Because temperatures decrease as altitude increases, mountain regions exhibit a wide variety of climate conditions and vegetation. Mountain ecosystems also vary depending on the nature of the terrain, the degree of exposure to sun and wind and the latitude at which they are located in temperate, subtropical or tropical regions.

Despite their rich biodiversity, mountain ecosystems are generally fragile. At high altitudes, many are battered by high winds and torrential rains, while others receive almost no precipitation. Other hazards include exposure to intense solar radiation and natural disasters such as avalanches, landslides, earthquakes and flash floods. The cooler temperatures of many mountain areas contribute to slow soil formation and vegetation growth, while the slopes facilitate erosion. Poor soil quality is typical of such environments.

Where mountain people live

FAO estimated the total number of mountain people at 718 million in 2000. Of these, 625 million live in developing countries and the CIS.

Sixty percent of the total mountain area in these countries is located at altitudes below 1 500 metres, and 70 percent of the mountain population lives there. By contrast, only 15 percent of the mountain area is situated above 3 500 metres, and only 2.5 percent of the population inhabits these heights.

Although urbanization and the growth of mountain cities is important in some regions, more than three-quarters of mountain people in developing countries and the CIS are still rural. Traditionally, they have obtained their livelihoods from a combination of agriculture, forestry, herding, hunting, fishing and collecting wild plants. Commodities particularly suited to commercial development in mountain ecosystems include indigenous grains, tree crops such as tea and apples, medicinal herbs and other forest products, and freshwater fish.

FAO estimates that about 40 percent of the mountain area in developing countries and the CIS produces less than 100 kg of cereals per person per year. Another 30 percent is covered by closed forests or nature preserves. Rural people living in such locations have difficulty obtaining an adequate livelihood from agriculture. FAO has used estimates of their number together with other qualitative information to arrive at a preliminary estimate of the number of mountain people who are vulnerable to food insecurity.

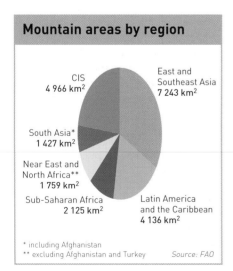

Mountain areas by region

CIS 4 966 km²
East and Southeast Asia 7 243 km²
South Asia* 1 427 km²
Near East and North Africa** 1 759 km²
Sub-Saharan Africa 2 125 km²
Latin America and the Caribbean 4 136 km²

* including Afghanistan
** excluding Afghanistan and Turkey   Source: FAO

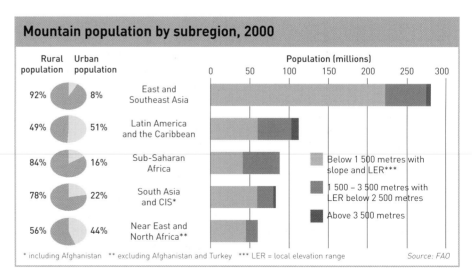

Mountain population by subregion, 2000

Rural population	Urban population		Population (millions)

East and Southeast Asia — Rural 92%, Urban 8%
Latin America and the Caribbean — Rural 49%, Urban 51%
Sub-Saharan Africa — Rural 84%, Urban 16%
South Asia and CIS* — Rural 78%, Urban 22%
Near East and North Africa** — Rural 56%, Urban 44%

Below 1 500 metres with slope and LER***
1 500 – 3 500 metres with LER below 2 500 metres
Above 3 500 metres

* including Afghanistan   ** excluding Afghanistan and Turkey   *** LER = local elevation range   Source: FAO

Vulnerability of mountain people

Based on information currently available, FAO estimates that more than half of the mountain population in developing and CIS countries (in the range of 250–370 million people) are vulnerable to food insecurity. (This estimate of vulnerability is not be confused with FAO's estimates of the undernourished population. Typically about half of those identified as vulnerable are actually undernourished.)

As noted above, mountain environments differ according to altitude, latitude and terrain. These differences influence both livelihood opportunities and sources of vulnerability for mountain people. Many other factors also play an important role, including the difficulty of access and relative isolation of many areas, the degree to which they are integrated into national societies, links between mountain regions and the national economy, and overall economic performance.

Cultural traditions in mountain regions are often strong and resilient. Yet lack of crop diversity and limited access to current information and knowledge about good nutrition and health care practices expose mountain people to high rates of

Vulnerable mountain people, by region, 2000

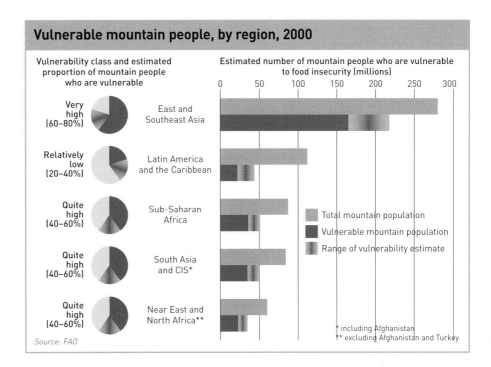

Source: FAO

malnutrition and disease. Traditional attitudes and beliefs may also lead people to maintain land-use practices that are no longer suitable to evolving conditions in mountain environments.

In many places traditional livelihood strategies are no longer sustainable because of mounting demographic pressure, rapid deforestation, erosion and loss of soil quality. Where this is so, conflict over control of increasingly scarce resources has become frequent.

Mountain cities offer economic opportunities but bring with them pollution, increased need for cash and weakening of indigenous highland institutions.

Resources and opportunities for vulnerable mountain people

Water – Water is an important natural resource found at high elevations. Mountain springs and snowmelt are the two main sources. Capturing the value of this resource is an important issue for mountain people, since much of the demand originates from people living in the surrounding lowlands. Use of mountain water for generating electricity, for irrigating crops, for sale as bottled water and for other industrial uses is common. However, conflict over water rights between downstream users and mountain peoples living at points of origin are increasingly frequent, and public policy is not adequate to deal with the issue.

Agriculture – Even though mountain water is plentiful, mountain land at higher elevations may be arid. In many areas, mountain farmers have developed quite sophisticated water management and

small-scale irrigation techniques. Where soil quality has been maintained or can be economically restored, crop agriculture remains a viable option. Livestock and aquaculture offer opportunities to diversify income and contribute high quality, protein products to mountain food systems.

Conservation and tourism – The natural beauty and biodiversity of many mountain environments offers good possibilities for the development of eco- and ethno-tourism, as well as for providing employment to caretakers in protected areas. Capital investment in infrastructure and training programmes to support the tourist industry will be required to realize these possibilities.

Forestry and pasturelands – The potential for forestry development in many mountain areas is high. Exploitation of this potential has been hampered, however, by the

pressing need of mountain people to use trees as a source of immediate cash income (for sale as firewood and lumber, or for grazing of livestock). Introduction of forest management practices that allow people to manage herds and maintain cash flow without cutting trees at an unsustainable rate is a prerequisite for success.

Mountain industry – Growth of urban centres is occurring naturally in some mountain areas and could be encouraged in others. Cities provide diverse employment opportunities to mountain people and can help to maintain the equilibrium between the mountain population and the carrying capacity of the natural resource base. Investing in the development of transport infrastructure and in industries that add value to local resources and reduce bulk prior to shipment to markets in non-mountain areas can contribute to healthy urbanization in mountain areas.

Special feature

Vulnerability and sustainability of mountain livelihood systems

FAO's study has focused on 18 mountain ranges that are home to almost 90 percent of mountain people in developing countries and the CIS. The analysis looks at a number of factors that determine the vulnerability and sustainability of mountain livelihoods. These factors include elevation, population density, degree of urbanization, land-use patterns, agricultural productivity and cultural traditions.

Maps on these pages depict the mountain areas by mountain class, the population density and the land-cover patterns and rainfed cereal production per person. Texts summarize the sources of vulnerability specific to each major mountain range and highlight actions that could help reduce vulnerability.

Latin America: Sierra Madre and Andes

In general, the 112 million mountain people of Latin America and the Caribbean are the most urbanized and least vulnerable in the developing world. The proximity of economically dynamic mountain cities opens up more income-generating options, but pockets of people at high elevations in the Andes remain isolated and extremely vulnerable. Rural mountain people in Central America and Mexico are also quite vulnerable. Agricultural land has been very unevenly distributed, restricting many farmers to tiny plots of land and forcing them to sell their labour to survive.

In the northern Andes, two-thirds of the mountain population live in or near large cities. Most rural mountain people practice intensive, commercial agriculture at moderate altitudes. On the lower slopes and valleys, coffee and horticultural crops are grown for local sale and export. In the higher valleys, maize, other temperate crops and pigs predominate. Vulnerability to food insecurity is relatively low.

Urbanization is also significant in the high Andes. Around half the mountain population lives in or near cities or on lower-elevation slopes where access to jobs and markets helps keep vulnerability relatively low. But the other half consists of extremely poor indigenous farming families, who grow traditional grains (quinoa) and potatoes and raise sheep and llamas in the steep valleys and vast, treeless tableland above 3 500 metres. Isolation, population pressure and soil erosion have seriously undermined their traditional livelihood systems and vulnerability is very high. Specialized markets exist for llama and alpaca wool, woven goods, quinoa and selected potato varieties. But the information and skills needed for effective participation are lacking.

In the Sierra Madre of Central America and Mexico, more than 40 percent of mountain people live in urban areas, where recent surveys indicate that the incidence of vulnerability is quite low. But most of the rural mountain population is not so fortunate. Farmers grow maize and beans and migrate seasonally to work as labourers on large coffee and sugar estates. But earnings are low and demand for migrant labour is declining. To cope, many families send members to cities and neighbouring countries to find jobs and send back remittances. And

Latin America: Sierra Madre and Andes

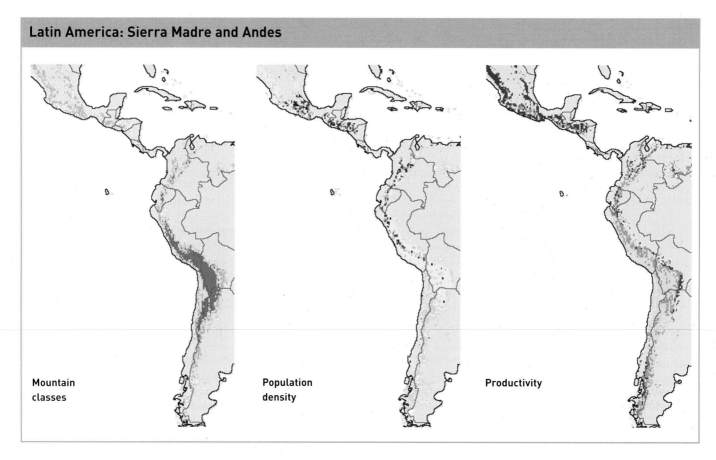

Mountain classes

Population density

Productivity

Eastern and southern Africa: Rift Valley

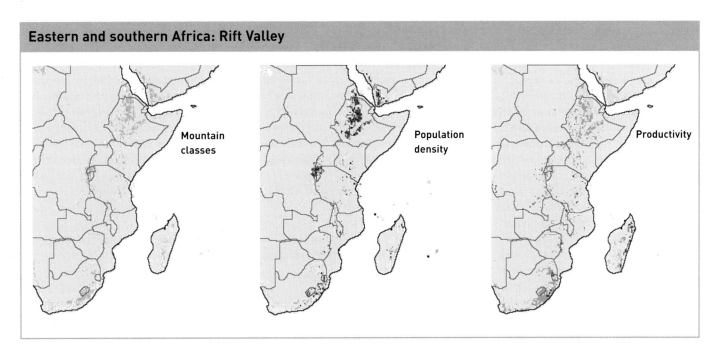

entire families are migrating to new areas and clearing forests to obtain land. Overall, the incidence of vulnerability in this subregion is quite high.

Mountain people in Latin America face a number of major challenges, including lack of access to land, unsustainable land-

Key to maps, pages 16–19

Mountain classes: elevation

- 300 – 1 000m and LER* > 300m
- 1 000 – 1 500 and slope > 5 or LER > 300m
- 1 500 – 2 500 and slope > 2
- 2 500 – 3 500
- 3 500 – 4 500
- > 4 500
- Non-mountain area

* LER = local elevation range

Source: UNEP-WCMC

Population density: people per km²

- 0
- 0 – 1
- 1 – 25
- 25 – 50
- 50 – 100
- 100 – 300
- > 300
- Non-mountain area

Source: LandScan2000/FAO

Productivity: rainfed crop production per person / other land use

- < 100 kg
- > 100 kg
- Closed forest
- Protected area
- Irrigated area (over 35%)
- Non-mountain area

Source: FAO/ UNEP-WCMC/ Univ. Kassel

use practices, poor integration of indigenous peoples into national societies and economies, and lack of technical skills.

Land reforms are being introduced in some countries. But they will only make a lasting impact on poverty and hunger if coupled with better agricultural extension and marketing services for small mountain farmers. The potential contributions of indigenous cultures to sustainable mountain development also need to be more widely recognized and supported. Likewise, new migrants in mountain cities will need support.

Eastern and southern Africa: Rift Valley

More than 90 percent of the 88 million mountain people in sub-Saharan Africa live in the ranges of the East African Rift at altitudes that rarely exceed 2 500 metres. Although these ranges include some of the most densely populated mountain areas in the world, less than 15 percent of the mountain population lives in cities and the incidence of vulnerability is quite high.

Almost half the mountain population in the region lives in the densely populated Ethiopian highlands. In an area frequently ravaged by drought, the traditional farming system, based on local grains, cattle, sheep and goats, cannot reliably support the existing or projected population. The number of landless peasants is growing and their future is very bleak. Vulnerability

to food insecurity is high. Long-term survival hinges on community-based action to strengthen non-farm activities and local infrastructure.

Population density is also extremely high in the mountains of Burundi, Rwanda and the eastern Democratic Republic of Congo. Deforestation and soil erosion are widespread and conflict between settled farmers and pastoralists can be intense. Vulnerability is quite high, but almost one-third of the mountain population lives in urban areas which provide more livelihood options. More sustainable management of farmland and open pastures, and reclamation of marshlands, could yield significant gains in food security if backed by strong efforts to improve infrastructure and extension services.

From Kenya to Zimbabwe, mountain and non-mountain people share a common farming system. All grow maize, tobacco, cotton and oilseeds for cash sale. But productivity has deteriorated since structural adjustment brought an end to fertilizer subsidies. Droughts, livestock diseases, scarcity of wild foods and the spread of HIV/AIDS have further destabilized this farming system. Although the incidence of vulnerability is now quite high, prospects for sustainable development are good if investments are made to improve management of soil and water resources and provide participatory extension and rural services.

Special feature

Near East and North Africa: Atlas, Zagros and Caucasus

The mountain population in the Near East and North Africa of 60 million people is the smallest in the developing world, and more than half live in cities. But farming and herding practised by rural mountain people from Morocco to Iran has become increasingly stressed, and vulnerability to food insecurity is quite high.

Most rural mountain people in the region plant cereal and fodder crops each autumn. The crops – mainly rainfed wheat, barley and legumes – lie dormant through the cold winter months before completing their growth in the spring. Tree crops, fruits, olives and vineyards are grown on terraces. Herds of goats and sheep are common throughout the region, often grazed on communally managed lands.

Environmental degradation, caused mainly by poor maintenance of terraces and overgrazing, is widespread. The resulting decline in productivity, combined with long distances to markets, increasing competition from subsidized food imports and growing incidence of drought, has led to increasing poverty and food insecurity. Many men are leaving mountain areas to find employment opportunities elsewhere and a significant number of households are likely to shift out of agriculture.

For those that remain, a number of measures could yield important gains in sustainability and food security. Improved watershed planning and management are needed to protect both existing levels of productivity and downstream rural and urban water users. Introduction of conservation tillage and better integration of crop and livestock production systems could boost both productivity and sustainability. More equitable regulation and control of common grazing resources (often officially classified as state forest) would also reduce both environmental damage and food insecurity. Action is also needed to facilitate land consolidation, forge stronger linkages between farm and off-farm economies and promote local off-farm employment.

South and Central Asia: Hindu Kush, Pamirs, Himalayas, Tibetan Plateau and Kunlun Mountains

Mountains dominate the landscape of Afghanistan, Pakistan, northern India, Nepal, Bhutan, northwestern China, and the Central Asian Republics. Although this region features the world's highest mountains and most populous countries, the mountain population of South and Central Asia is not much larger than that of the East African Rift. Nearly 90 percent of the mountain people inhabit the high ranges in the north. The vast majority are rural and live at elevations below 3 500 metres, where they practise various combinations of crop agriculture and herding. The incidence of vulnerability is quite high, exacerbated, as elsewhere, by increasing population pressure and environmental degradation.

Deforestation poses a major threat. As populations grow, remaining forests are being cut down at a rapid rate to open up new agricultural land. This leads to soil erosion and depletion of soil moisture, reducing productivity and forcing women to walk ever longer distances for fuelwood and water.

Traditional cultures are deeply rooted and often dictate local practices governing the use of land, water and forests. But with many men migrating away, social cohesion in some areas is breaking down, making it more difficult to resolve disputes over land ownership and use of common resources. The role of women as farmers and social leaders has become increasingly important. Improving their access to training and resources will be critical for overcoming environmental, economic and social problems.

Although higher altitudes also suffer from serious erosion, population density is lower and people have more livelihood options. Many families graze livestock on higher slopes and supplement their farm income with cross-border trade, tourism and mountaineering. The incidence of vulnerability is still quite high, however.

The pastoral system predominates in mountain areas in Central Asia, as well as in non-mountainous high flatlands. Sheep and cattle are grazed on open pastures in high areas or adjacent dry zones, while cereals, fodder crops and potatoes are cultivated for subsistence in mountain valleys. Meat and wool production are the main sources of income from this system. But excessive animal population and poor grazing techniques have caused serious erosion and degradation of open pastures. Wool production has fallen sharply and vulnerability to food insecurity is now quite high. Restoration and sustainable management of grazing land are essential for improving conditions.

Near East: Zagros and Caucasus

Mountain classes

Population density

Productivity

South and Central Asia: Hindu Kush, Pamirs, Himalayas, Tibetan Plateau and Kunlun Mountains

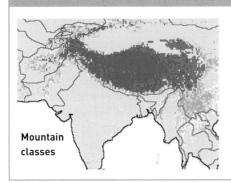

Mountain classes

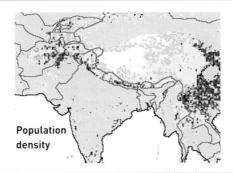

Population density

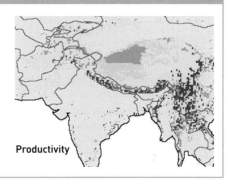

Productivity

East and Southeast Asia: Ningling Shan and Truong Son

Although not nearly as tall or as famous as the Himalayas and the Hindu Kush, the mountains of East and Southeast Asia are vast and far more heavily populated. Nearly half of all the mountain people in the developing countries and the CIS live in the mountains of southern China, the Indochinese Peninsula and the larger Pacific islands. For the most part, these areas are both densely populated and overwhelmingly rural, with very few people living in cities. As a result, landholdings are extremely small, crop production per person is low, and farmers are increasingly moving into marginal sloping lands to survive. The number of people living in forests and protected areas is also quite large. Vulnerability to food insecurity is very high, probably affecting 170 to 220 million people.

Crop and farm production intensity varies considerably. In southern China, mountain farmers have developed sophisticated terracing and water management techniques and make effective use of crop and animal wastes to preserve soil quality. Elsewhere, intensive production technologies are less developed and productivity is lower. Vulnerability is more widespread.

Two distinct farming systems are found throughout the region. At moderate altitudes with gentle slopes, farmers grow a wide variety of crops, with rice used as the staple in the south and wheat in the north. Livestock are used as draught animals, for meat and as wealth. Pigs and poultry provide an important source of cash income. This system can be highly productive, as demonstrated by the mountain farmers of southern China, whose intensive farming also benefits from good links to markets where they can buy inputs and sell produce. In other locations, semi-subsistence farming with limited sales is common. These areas can also be highly productive, if supported by investments in infrastructure and participatory extension.

On higher slopes in tropical areas, tribal groups farm extensively through both permanent and shifting cultivation. Typically, they supplement their crops by grazing cattle and buffalo in the forests and gathering other forest products for home use. Poor soil quality, low levels of inputs and isolation from markets constrain progress, and poverty and food insecurity are widespread. Improved forestry management and agroforestry offer the best prospects for improving conditions.

East and Southeast Asia: Ningling Shan and Truong Son

Mountain classes

Population density

Productivity

Towards the Summit commitments

Acting to combat hunger

Rehabilitating degraded lands

In most developing countries, hunger is concentrated in degraded and marginal areas. Concerted efforts to rehabilitate degraded lands and use appropriate technology have yielded remarkable gains in productivity and food security in a number of countries.

In China, the government has rehabilitated 5 million ha of low- and medium-yielding land since 1996. Soil fertility has been improved through better farming practices, expanded irrigation facilities and increased use of organic fertilizers. Crop yields in these areas increased by 2 200 kg per ha on average, spurring gains in both incomes and food security.

China has also expanded animal raising and fish farming in barren hills, grasslands, and coastal areas that are better suited to grazing and aquaculture than to intensive agriculture. Livestock and aquaculture production increased by almost 20 percent between 1996 and 1998, significantly improving the diversity of both diets and incomes.

In India, a watershed development project successfully brought nearly 1 000 ha of severely degraded land back into production, improving food security and sustainability in an area where 52 percent of all households lived below the poverty line.

Water availability was also enhanced considerably, allowing farmers to expand irrigated areas from 11 percent to 79 percent of the total cultivated land. Farmers were able to start growing high-yielding, high-value crops that require more reliable water supplies, such as wheat, groundnuts, soybeans and vegetables. Average crop yields increased more than ten-fold and farmers more than doubled the average number of crops grown on the available land, from 0.7 to 1.7 crops per year.

The higher productivity helped boost farmers' incomes by over 600 percent. Employment generated by the scheme helped landless members of the community increase their income from less than US$40 to US$360 per year – a ninefold gain in a span of just seven years.

Increasing rice production

Rice was one of the first crops to benefit from Green Revolution technology. But productivity gains began to slow in the early 1990s, falling below the rate of population growth.

In partnership with other international, regional and national organizations and research institutes, the International Rice Commission has mobilized a campaign to reverse declining trends in productivity on a sustainable basis. Key elements of the campaign include:
- technical support for the development and use of hybrid rice outside China;
- rapid transfer of improved rice technologies to farmers in West Africa;
- Integrated Rice Crop Management for sustainable rice production.

Efforts to increase rice production have scored significant gains in West Africa, where rice is the staple food for most of the population (see graph).

The West African Rice Development Association (WARDA), has succeeded in crossing hardy African rice species with

Meeting the challenge of land degradation

Land degradation threatens the sustainability of both agricultural production and food security in many developing countries. A recently completed study of human-induced soil degradation in Asia found that almost 20 percent of all land suffers from moderate to extreme degradation in the 17 countries that were covered. Agricultural productivity is greatly reduced on moderately degraded land. Land where degradation is classified as strong or extreme has been largely and irreversibly destroyed and can no longer be reclaimed for farming.

Combating land degradation, as China and India have done in the projects described here, could relieve the pressures that create vulnerability, reduce productivity and worsen poverty in marginal areas.

Extent and proportion of land classified as moderately to extremely degraded, 1997

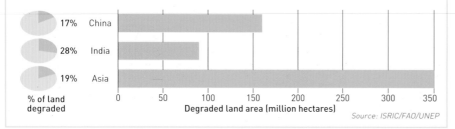

Source: ISRIC/FAO/UNEP

Increasing rice yields

Annual average, 1994–2000

Côte d'Ivoire
Togo
Gambia
Niger
Mali
World average

% increase

Source: FAO

higher-yielding species imported from Asia. The offspring of this scientific breakthrough is New Rice for Africa (NERICA), varieties that can out-compete weeds, resist many African insect pests, and tolerate disease, drought and acid soils.

Research shows that NERICA can increase yields in the area's uplands and rainfed lowland areas significantly – by 25 percent with low inputs and by as much as 250 percent with a minimal increase in fertilizer use. UNDP has reported that adoption of NERICA could increase production in West Africa by 250 000–750 000 tonnes per year and save the region up to US$187 million per year on its import bill.

Diversifying income

The Co-operative Dairy Development Programme in Bangladesh has demonstrated that a sound diversification programme can improve food security by creating income and employment-generating opportunities. The programme targeted small farmers and the landless with a package of technologies, training and infrastructure support to improve and expand milk production, collection, processing and distribution.

The cooperative started modestly with 4 300 very poor, landless households. It has now grown into a thriving enterprise, involving 40 000 farmers organized into 390 primary cooperatives. In addition to the cooperative members themselves, the programme has improved the livelihoods and nutritional status of an estimated 300 000 family members and nearly 2 000 people employed by the cooperatives, dairy plants and offices.

Regular earnings from milk have increased ten-fold in real terms to US$0.65 a day, helping to lift household earnings well above the poverty line.

Extending micro-credit

Tunisia has combined micro-credit and social safety nets to help poor rural households, elderly and disabled people and other vulnerable groups. The National Fund for Solidarity and the Tunisian State Bank for Solidarity provide micro-credit to small producers, especially women. The government has also

guaranteed access to basic social services, increased the minimum wage in rural areas and maintained affordable prices for basic foodstuffs. Safety net programmes have improved the food security and nutritional status of more than 114 000 families.

Mexico has also improved access to credit in rural areas. The Programme of Direct Payments to the Countryside (PROCAMPO) was designed to help farmers during the country's 15-year, planned transition to free trade after the North American Free Trade Agreement of 1994. The programme covers an average of 14 million ha of farmland each year and reaches nearly 3 million producers. In the year 2000 alone, PROCAMPO provided payments of over US$1 billion, with an average of US$68 per hectare.

Forty-five percent of beneficiaries are small producers who had previously been unable to invest adequately to improve their productivity and income. Overall, every peso of PROCAMPO payments generated another two pesos of income.

Realizing the right to food

At the World Food Summit: *five years later*, 182 heads of state and government or their representatives reaffirmed that everyone has the right to have access

to safe and nutritious food. The final Summit declaration invited the FAO Council to establish an Intergovernmental Working Group, with the participation of stakeholders, charged with elaborating voluntary guidelines to support countries in their efforts to "achieve the progressive realization of the right to adequate food in the context of national food security".

The World Food Summit in 1996 invigorated efforts to translate the right to food from a moral imperative into a clear and enforceable right under national and international law. At the national level, over 20 countries have included the right to food specifically in their constitutions. South Africa, for example, has incorporated the right to food into its Constitution as part of its Bill of Rights. All economic and social rights have been declared enforceable through the courts under South African law.

South Africa is one of several countries that organized national seminars during 2002, seeking ways to implement the right to food at the national level. Other seminars have been held or are planned in Brazil, Uganda, Mali, Nepal, Norway and Germany. A synthesis of the lessons learned from the seminars held during 2002 will provide the basis for other nations to launch similar efforts.

CFS reviews and spurs progress towards WFS goals

The Intergovernmental Committee on World Food Security (CFS) is the UN forum for monitoring progress towards the 1996 World Food Summit (WFS) goals and recommending actions that could help achieve them more rapidly. At its 28th Session, held at FAO headquarters in Rome from 6 to 9 June 2002, the CFS:

• noted that the decline in the number of hungry people has fallen far short of the pace needed to achieve the WFS target of reducing the number by half no later than 2015;

• encouraged countries to monitor progress more closely as part of the process being established to follow all of the Human Development Goals endorsed at the Millennium Summit in 2000;

• backed a twin-track strategy proposed jointly by FAO, IFAD and WFP for

reducing, and eventually eliminating, food insecurity and poverty. The strategy combines emergency action to give millions of hungry people access to food with longer-term measures to stimulate agriculture, rural development and sustainable livelihoods. The Committee cited supplying food assistance programmes from local production as an example of "maximum synergy" that can expand market opportunities, farm output and employment, while providing food to the hungry;

• prepared the ground for a call issued the following week by the World Food Summit: *five years later* for countries to establish voluntary guidelines for achieving "the progressive realization of the right to adequate food in the context of national food security".

Towards the Summit commitments

Addressing the risk factors common to conflict and food insecurity

ONFLICT is one of the most common causes of food insecurity. The displacement of people and disruption of agricultural production and food distribution leave tens of millions of people at risk of hunger and famine. War and civil strife were cited as major causes in 15 of the 44 countries that suffered exceptional food emergencies during 2001 and the first quarter of 2002. Conversely, food insecurity may lead to or exacerbate conflict, particularly when compounded by other shocks and stresses. The interface between food insecurity and conflict has critical implications for food security and conflict prevention programmes alike.

Conflict as a cause of food insecurity

One of the most direct effects of conflict on food security is the displacement of people. In 2001, there were more than 12 million refugees, 25 million internally displaced people (IDPs) and an unknown number of people trapped in combat zones. Most of these people need temporary food assistance until they can return to their homes and fields or find new livelihoods. More than 30 percent of the recipients of food aid from the World Food Programme in 2000 were refugees, IDPs and returnees.

Conflict is also a major cause of structural food insecurity. Armed conflict may prevent farmers from producing food and may cut off access to food by disrupting transport, trade and markets. According to FAO, conflict in sub-Saharan Africa resulted in losses of almost US$52 billion in agricultural output between 1970 and 1997, a figure equivalent to 75 percent of all official development assistance received by the conflict-affected countries. Estimated losses in agricultural output for all developing countries averaged US$4.3 billion per year – enough to have raised the food intake of 330 million undernourished people to minimum required levels.

Conflict, often combined with drought, triggered six of the seven major African famines since 1980. Early warning and response usually prevent famine arising from drought and other natural disasters. But in war zones, lack of security and disruption of transport and social networks impede delivery of relief aid.

Risk factors underlying both food insecurity and conflict

While the impact of conflict on food security can be identified and quantified with some degree of certainty, the way in which food insecurity contributes to conflict is more indirect. What can be documented is that food insecurity and conflict tend to be prevalent in the same locations (see graph) and that they are both consequences of a common set of risk factors (see chart).

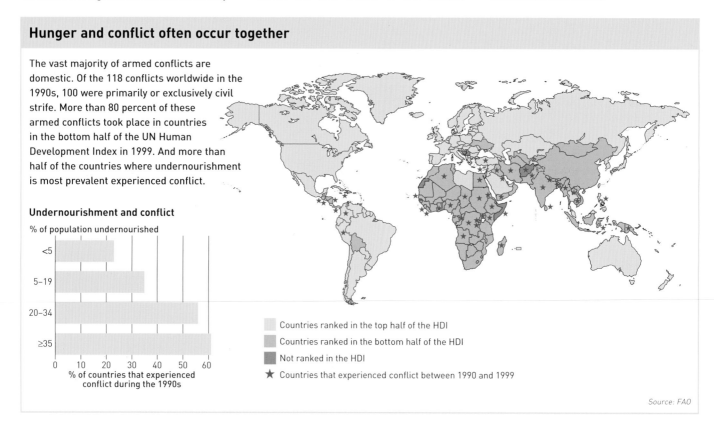

Hunger and conflict often occur together

The vast majority of armed conflicts are domestic. Of the 118 conflicts worldwide in the 1990s, 100 were primarily or exclusively civil strife. More than 80 percent of these armed conflicts took place in countries in the bottom half of the UN Human Development Index in 1999. And more than half of the countries where undernourishment is most prevalent experienced conflict.

Undernourishment and conflict

% of population undernourished

(bar chart with categories <5, 5–19, 20–34, ≥35; x-axis 0 to 60)

% of countries that experienced conflict during the 1990s

Countries ranked in the top half of the HDI
Countries ranked in the bottom half of the HDI
Not ranked in the HDI
★ Countries that experienced conflict between 1990 and 1999

Source: FAO

5 *"We will endeavour to prevent and be prepared for natural disasters and man-made emergencies and to meet transitory and emergency food requirements ..."*

1 *"We will ensure an enabling environment designed to create conditions for the eradication of poverty and for durable peace ..."*

Some analysts have argued that underdevelopment and poverty, which are closely related to food insecurity, make countries more prone to conflict. As evidence, they point to the fact that more than 80 percent of wars and civil strife in recent years have taken place in countries ranked in the lower half of the United Nations Human Development Index (HDI) (see map).

Others contend that objective measures of social grievance, such as inequality, lack of democracy and ethnic and religious divisions have no systematic effect on conflict risk. One analysis of civil wars from 1965 to 1999 concludes that conflict risk is mainly correlated with the degree to which rebels believe they can fare well out of war.

Still others emphasize the rapid loss of livelihood as a key common denominator in many recent internal wars. Disillusioned, frustrated young men, unable to reach a status in life that earlier generations had achieved, are easily and cheaply recruited by warlords.

Yet another important factor contributing to both food insecurity and conflict is environmental scarcity. Degradation or depletion of natural resources, unequal distribution and population pressure can trigger competition for scarce resources, in particular arable land and water. Increasing competition for resources may spur farmers to abandon sustainable methods and exploit marginal lands in a desperate effort to secure their incomes and feed their families. When this process leads to deepened poverty, large-scale migration, sharpened social cleavages and weakened institutions, the depleted environment and resulting food insecurity become fertile ground for conflict.

Common risks require coordinated action

Food insecurity and conflict feed upon a common set of risk factors, which they can also exacerbate. If war-related hunger is to be reduced, development aid is not to be consumed in conflict and food is not inadvertently to become a factor in fuelling conflict, a concerted effort is needed to make conflict prevention an integral part of food security

The interface between violent conflict and food insecurity

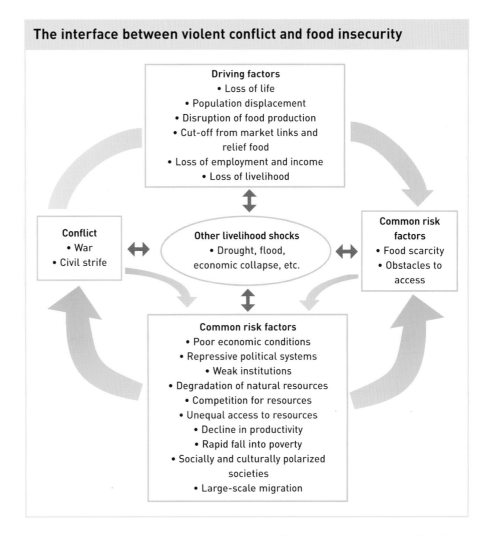

Driving factors
- Loss of life
- Population displacement
- Disruption of food production
- Cut-off from market links and relief food
- Loss of employment and income
- Loss of livelihood

Conflict
- War
- Civil strife

Other livelihood shocks
- Drought, flood, economic collapse, etc.

Common risk factors
- Food scarcity
- Obstacles to access

Common risk factors
- Poor economic conditions
- Repressive political systems
- Weak institutions
- Degradation of natural resources
- Competition for resources
- Unequal access to resources
- Decline in productivity
- Rapid fall into poverty
- Socially and culturally polarized societies
- Large-scale migration

and agriculture policy and programming in conflict-prone areas.

Assessing and addressing the risk factors common to food insecurity and conflict, as well as the livelihood dynamics in conflict-prone areas, can serve as a mechanism both for preventing conflict and reducing hunger.

Measures to address common risk factors

- Incorporating conflict prevention and mitigation into regional food security strategies and policies.
- Mainstreaming conflict prevention in food security and agricultural investment programmes in conflict-prone countries.
- Profiling vulnerable livelihood groups to identify disparities among them that might trigger conflict.
- Implementing programmes so as to minimize rivalry for aid resources and benefits and to foster cooperation among rival communities or groups.
- Protecting the natural resource base and promoting equitable access to resources through effective, sustainable institutions.

- Integrating conflict analysis and conflict indicators into traditional food security early warning systems.
- Monitoring crisis potential in resource-poor areas and, in particular: the state of key livelihood systems; the interests and concerns of the principal social or political groups; and the preparedness of communal, country-level or international organizations to prevent hunger and conflict and provide support services to resource-poor households.
- Assessing the impact of food and agricultural programmes on the various stakeholders in conflict contexts and on the development of the conflict itself.

Towards the Summit commitments

Confronting the causes of malnutrition: the hidden challenge of micronutrient deficiencies

OVER 2 BILLION PEOPLE worldwide suffer from micronutrient malnutrition, often called "hidden hunger". Their diets supply inadequate amounts of vitamins and minerals such as vitamin A, iron, iodine, zinc, folate, selenium and vitamin C. Deficiencies usually occur when the habitual diet lacks diversity and does not include sufficient quantities of the fruits, vegetables, dairy products, meat and fish that are the best sources of many micronutrients.

Micronutrients are essential for human growth and development as well as normal functioning. The three most common forms of micronutrient malnutrition are deficiencies of vitamin A, iodine and iron. In developing countries, deficiencies of micronutrients often are not present in isolation but exist in combination (see map).

Children and women are the most vulnerable to micronutrient deficiencies – children because of the critical importance of micronutrients for normal growth and development, women because of their higher need for iron, especially during child-bearing years and pregnancy.

Between 100 and 140 million children suffer from vitamin A deficiency. That figure includes more than 2 million children each year afflicted with severe visual problems, of whom an estimated 250 000 to 500 000 are permanently blinded.

Lack of vitamin A also impairs the immune system, greatly increasing the risk of illness and death from common childhood infections such as diarrhoea and measles (see graph).

The most devastating consequence of iodine deficiency is reduced mental capacity. Some 20 million people world-wide are mentally handicapped as a result of iodine deficiency, including 100 000 born each year with irreversible brain damage because their mothers lacked iodine prior to and during pregnancy.

Iron deficiency and the anaemia it causes are the most widespread of all forms of micronutrient malnutrition. Anaemia results in fatigue, dizziness and breathlessness following exertion.

Children with anaemia are less able to concentrate and have less energy for play and exploratory behaviours. In adults, anaemia diminishes work capacity and productivity by as much as 10–15 percent (see graph, page 11). And for pregnant women, anaemia substantially increases the risk of death in childbirth, accounting for up to 20 percent of maternal deaths in Asia and Africa.

The three main strategies for reducing micronutrient deficiencies are dietary diversity and food fortification along with supplements.

Most micronutrient deficiencies could be eliminated by modifying diets to include a greater diversity of nutrient-rich foods. Promoting home gardens, community fish ponds, and livestock and poultry production can contribute to increasing dietary diversity, while improving food supplies and incomes at the same time (see box on dietary diversification).

Another important food-based strategy is food fortification. The most successful of these initiatives is fortification of salt with iodine (see box). Other micronutrients can also be supplied to populations by enriching widely consumed foods such as milk and flour. In addition,

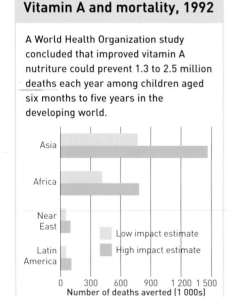

Vitamin A and mortality, 1992

A World Health Organization study concluded that improved vitamin A nutriture could prevent 1.3 to 2.5 million deaths each year among children aged six months to five years in the developing world.

Number of deaths averted (1 000s)

- Low impact estimate
- High impact estimate

Source: WHO

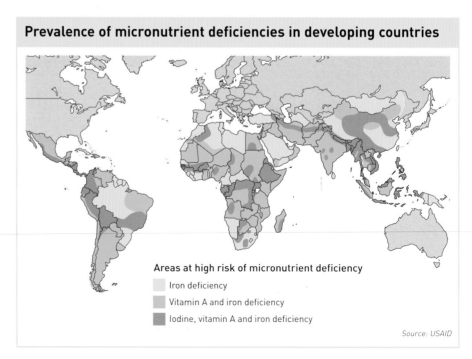

Prevalence of micronutrient deficiencies in developing countries

Areas at high risk of micronutrient deficiency

- Iron deficiency
- Vitamin A and iron deficiency
- Iodine, vitamin A and iron deficiency

Source: USAID

recent advances in crop breeding and biotechnology have heightened the prospects for "biofortification" – developing crops with higher concentrations of micronutrients (see box).

Supplementation involves treating and preventing micronutrient deficiencies by administering capsules, tablets, syrups or other preparations. This medical approach is the method of choice when the deficiency is severe and life-threatening or when access to regular intake of the deficient micronutrient is limited. Use of high-dose vitamin A supplements can reduce mortality from acute measles by up to 50 percent.

Successful campaigns to eliminate micronutrient deficiencies often combine all of these strategies. Vitamin A intake, for example, can best be increased over the long term by adding nutrient-rich foods to the diet and fortifying staple foods, while providing supplements to high-risk groups in vulnerable areas.

Dietary diversification reduces vitamin A deficiency

A home gardening programme focusing on production and consumption of vegetables rich in vitamin A and its precursor, beta carotene, has been successfully demonstrated by the Medical Research Council of South Africa in a mountainous, rural village in KwaZulu-Natal.

Prior to the programme, the diet of children in the village consisted mainly of maize porridge, bread and rice. The lack of variety and vitamin-rich foods resulted in high incidence of vitamin A deficiency. The programme changed that by promoting cultivation of vegetables, such as carrots, pumpkins and spinach, that are rich in beta carotene and by teaching villagers, especially women, the importance of including them regularly in their diet.

After only one year, the percentage of children consuming vitamin-A rich vegetables had increased significantly. And the increased diversity in their diets led to measurable improvements in vitamin A status.

Home gardens boost consumption of micronutrient-rich food

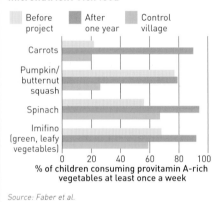

Source: Faber et al.

Biofortification increases nutrient content of staple foods

Both conventional plant breeding techniques and genetic engineering can be used to develop varieties of staple food crops that are enriched with essential minerals.

"Golden rice" offered proof that biotechnology can produce both nutrients and controversy. Golden rice owes its colour and its name to beta carotene, introduced by transplanting genes from daffodils and bacteria. Critics have charged that the enriched rice will not provide enough beta carotene to satisfy vitamin A requirements. But supporters argue that it could provide 15 to 20 percent of daily requirements and significantly reduce the incidence and severity of vitamin A deficiency, particularly if consumed in conjunction with other nutrient-rich foods.

Conventional plant breeding also holds promise for enhancing the nutrient content of staple foods. Varieties of crops differ considerably in the quantities of nutrients that they contain (see graph). Advances in plant breeding techniques and biotechnology may make it possible to cross varieties that are relatively rich in micronutrients with high-yielding varieties preferred by farmers.

Varietal differences suggest high biofortification potential for rice

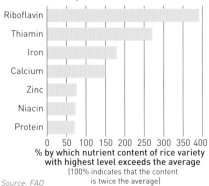

Source: FAO

Iodine deficiency disorders

Iodine deficiency disorder (IDD) is particularly prevalent in the mountainous regions of the world.

The areas with the most severe deficiencies include the Himalayas, the Andes, the European Alps and the vast mountains of China. IDD is also common in frequently flooded lowlands. In both mountains and flooded areas, iodine that is naturally present in the soil is leached away, reducing the iodine content in locally grown crops.

Iodization of salt has virtually eliminated IDD in the mountainous regions of industrialized countries in Europe and North America. Three-quarters of the countries in the developing world have enacted legislation for iodizing salt, mostly over the past 15 years. More than two-thirds of households now get adequately iodized salt. But access varies considerably (see graph below). Increasing access to iodized salt and improving quality control of its iodine content hold the key to eliminating iodine deficiency worldwide.

Access to iodized salt, 1995–98

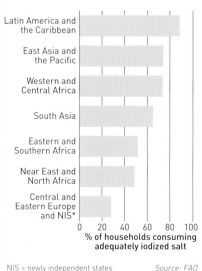

NIS = newly independent states   Source: FAO

Land reform and secure land tenure: keys to food security and sustainable rural development

PROVIDING SECURE ACCESS to land for the rural poor represents one of the key factors in achieving food security and sustainable agricultural development.

Poverty profile by landholding

More than 45 percent of the rural population of Bangladesh own less than one-quarter of a hectare of land. And more than half of these landless and near-landless farm families live in extreme poverty.

Share of rural population by farm size, 1988–89

Headcount index of poverty, 1988–89

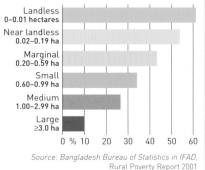

Source: Bangladesh Bureau of Statistics in IFAD, Rural Poverty Report 2001

Farm size and land productivity

A study in India (1971) confirmed that small farms produce around twice as much per hectare as large farms.

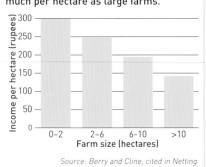

Source: Berry and Cline, cited in Netting

Nearly three-quarters of the world's poor and hungry live in rural areas in the developing world. Not surprisingly, severe poverty and hunger are concentrated among those who are landless or farm plots too small to provide for their needs.

More than 30 percent of the rural poor in Latin America and the Caribbean are landless. A study in Bangladesh found that more than half of all landless and near-landless rural households live in extreme poverty. By contrast, only 10 percent of farmers with more than 3 ha of land experienced extreme poverty (see graph). Numerous other studies have confirmed that reduction in or loss of access to land leads directly to reduced income and access to food.

For the poor and hungry in rural areas, access to land resources tends to be both inadequate and insecure. Many work as tenants or sharecroppers. Impoverished smallholders face the constant threat that they may be forced to sell their land and other assets to buy food.

Lack of secure rights to land perpetuates poverty and hunger. And vice versa. Food insecurity often drives poor farmers to make decisions that may jeopardize their ability to retain control of their land. Farmers who are struggling to feed their families are frequently forced to choose between short-term survival and longer-term economic and environmental sustainability – between buying food or fertilizer, for example, or between growing subsistence foods or potentially profitable commercial crops. Studies in Chile, Guatemala and Paraguay found that a boom in non-traditional export crops led to a significant loss of land by food-insecure smallholders, who were unable or unwilling to shift from subsistence production to cash crops.

Secure land tenure is also essential to sustainability. Without land that could be used as collateral, smallholders often cannot obtain the credit they need to maintain and improve their land. Nor can they be confident they would benefit from

their efforts, since they may lose rights to the land. Failure to invest in improved soil and water management results in land degradation and soil loss, threatening both the livelihoods of millions of people and future food security.

Land reform and reduction of poverty and hunger

Numerous studies confirm that improving access to land can have a major impact on reducing poverty and hunger. An exhaustive analysis in India found "a robust link between land reform and poverty reduction". The study examined the history of land reform efforts initiated at the state level between 1948 and 1990 and compared rates of poverty reduction and overall economic growth between states that had instituted meaningful land reforms and those that had not. The study confirmed that land reform significantly reduced rural poverty and stimulated growth in agricultural wages. Both smallholders and the landless labourers who constitute a major fraction of the rural poor benefited.

Another study of data from 20 developing countries found that concentration of land ownership explained 69 percent of the variation in poverty levels.

Analysis of FAO data suggests that food security and land distribution are also related. Developing countries where land was more equally distributed in 1980 have made more rapid progress in reducing the prevalence of hunger over the past two decades (see graph, next page).

Land reform and higher productivity

Improving access to land and reducing the concentration of land ownership yield benefits that extend far beyond the farmers themselves. Small farms in poor areas are usually more productive and efficient than large estates (see graph). Smallholders typically put far more labour into their fields. They are far more likely to plant more than one crop per year on their plots. And they rarely leave land lying idle, as is often the case on larger estates.

In Brazil, for example, less than 15 percent of the land on estates larger than 1 000 ha is planted in crops. A study in northeast Brazil found that output per hectare was 5.6 times higher on farms of 10–50 ha than on farms of more than 100 ha. In other countries, small farms have commonly been found to produce two to three times as much per hectare as large commercial estates.

Even poor people who remain landless benefit from more equal distribution of land. Small farms generally employ more people per hectare. And the income generated is more likely to be spent on local, non-farm products that provide employment for the landless and land poor.

The impact extends to the national level. A World Bank analysis of land distribution and GDP shows that countries with more equal distribution of land have achieved more rapid and sustained economic growth (see graph).

New directions and momentum

People who have rights to land are more able to enjoy a sustainable livelihood than those who have only partial rights of access. And those who have partial rights are, in general, better off than those who are landless. To promote rural development many countries are stressing the importance of improved access to land and increased tenure security.

Tenure reform has long been on the

Indigenous rights

Several countries in Latin America have undertaken major initiatives to recognize and protect the land rights of indigenous people. Particularly in lowlands, large areas have been recognized as inalienable territories that are collectively owned and, in some countries, self-governed by the indigenous population. Secure tenure for indigenous people has been recognized as an important precondition for effective conservation and sustainable management of tropical forests.

Bolivia and Colombia have pioneered formal agreements between environmental agencies and indigenous authorities to share responsibility for managing protected areas. In highland areas, indigenous landholdings are highly fragmented, making it more difficult to recognize collective ownership. But some titling projects have proved successful.

Keys to success included baseline studies that took indigenous tenure into account, backed up by land agencies with the political will and capacity to demarcate and title the land. Indigenous communities have also undertaken innovative initiatives for sustainable development by producing their own maps detailing customary land use, occupancy and knowledge of natural resource management.

Women's rights

In much of the developing world, women produce most of the food consumed by their families and communities. Yet women rarely have secure tenure to the land they work. A study in India, Nepal and Thailand, for example, found that less than 10 percent of women farmers own land.

Although traditional land tenure systems rarely granted women outright ownership of land, they frequently protected their rights to work and manage enough land to provide for their families' needs. In many cases, those rights are now being eroded by changing socio-economic conditions, land shortages and titling programmes that fail to recognize the value either of customary tenure practices or of women's contributions to agriculture.

Improving access to land for women is essential to increase both food security and sustainable production. Without secure tenure, women lack both the collateral and the security to improve the land they work and to invest in new technology. Yet numerous studies confirm that women dedicate more of their land and labour to producing staple foods and more of their income to providing for their families.

international agenda. Rather than a traditional top-down approach, however, modern reforms emphasize participatory, decentralized approaches that target disadvantaged groups, particularly indigenous groups and women (see boxes) and facilitate land market transactions, including leasing.

Land distribution linked to progress in reducing hunger and to economic growth

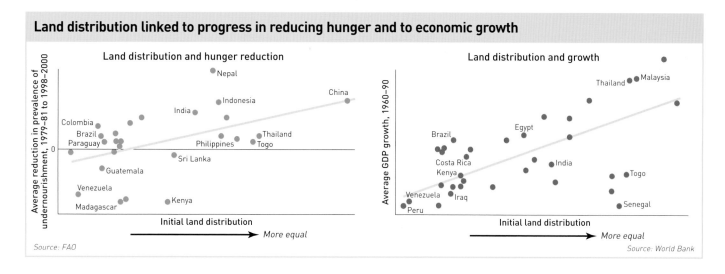

Land distribution and hunger reduction

Average reduction in prevalence of undernourishment, 1979–81 to 1998–2000

Nepal, China, Indonesia, India, Colombia, Brazil, Paraguay, Thailand, Philippines, Togo, Sri Lanka, Guatemala, Venezuela, Madagascar, Kenya

Initial land distribution — More equal

Source: FAO

Land distribution and growth

Average GDP growth, 1960–90

Thailand, Malaysia, Egypt, Brazil, Costa Rica, Kenya, India, Venezuela, Iraq, Peru, Togo, Senegal

Initial land distribution — More equal

Source: World Bank

Towards the Summit commitments

Financing for development: the critical role of hunger reduction and agricultural development

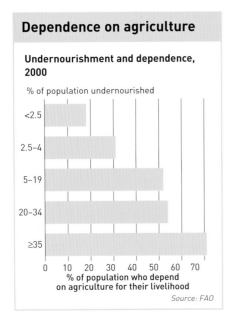

Dependence on agriculture

Undernourishment and dependence, 2000

% of population undernourished

Horizontal axis: % of population who depend on agriculture for their livelihood (0, 10, 20, 30, 40, 50, 60, 70)

Categories: <2.5, 2.5–4, 5–19, 20–34, ≥35

Source: FAO

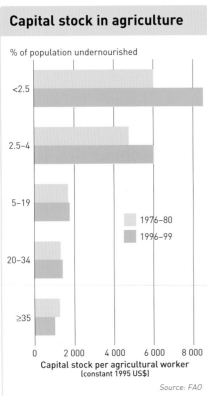

Capital stock in agriculture

% of population undernourished

Legend: 1976–80, 1996–99

Horizontal axis: Capital stock per agricultural worker (constant 1995 US$) (0, 2 000, 4 000, 6 000, 8 000)

Categories: <2.5, 2.5–4, 5–19, 20–34, ≥35

Source: FAO

THE SUMMIT-LEVEL CONFERENCE on Financing for Development convened by the United Nations in March 2002 marked a new level of commitment to the goals set by the Millennium Declaration of September 2000. These Millennium Development Goals restated and consolidated the commitments made by the international community at a series of conferences and summits that took place in the 1990s. Reducing human misery and promoting social development are the heart of the commitments. And reducing both extreme poverty and hunger by half by the year 2015 constitutes an overarching goal.

The Conference on Financing for Development proposed concrete actions in a number of areas aimed at increasing the level of resources mobilized for development and poverty reduction.

The three Rome-based UN agencies concerned with food, agriculture and rural development presented compelling arguments for giving priority to reducing hunger and supporting agricultural and rural development. FAO, the World Food Programme and the International Fund for Agricultural Development documented the debilitating effects of hunger on both individual productivity and overall economic growth. They showed clearly that, unless hunger is dealt with effectively, prospects for achieving other goals, such as universal education, maternal health and environmental sustainability, will be severely compromised (see pages 10–11).

The Rome-based agencies also offered evidence that combating hunger and extreme poverty requires renewed and expanded commitment to agriculture and rural development. Overall, some 70 percent of the poor in developing countries live in rural areas and derive their livelihoods from agriculture directly or indirectly. This dependence on agriculture is greater in those countries where hunger is most prevalent (see graph). Growth of the agricultural sector, therefore, is essential to reducing poverty and ensuring food security.

Investment in agriculture lags where hunger is most prevalent

An overview of the data on private investment, public expenditures and external assistance to agriculture in developing countries shows that the sector receives less investment and support in the very countries where hunger and poverty are widespread.

Most of the investment required to stimulate growth in the agricultural sector comes from private sources, mainly farmers themselves. A look at capital stock per agricultural worker in the primary agriculture of developing countries shows that it is extremely low and stagnant in countries where prevalence of undernourishment is high, as compared to those that have managed to reduce hunger (see graph).

And the investment gap is growing. Good performers in hunger reduction have had strong growth in capital stock in agriculture since 1975. In all other categories, investment has increased little, if at all. And in the group of countries where more than one-third of the people are undernourished, the value of capital stock in primary agriculture has declined in real terms over the past quarter century (see graph).

Public investment fails to reflect the importance of agriculture

Public investment in infrastructure, agricultural research, education and extension is essential in stimulating private investment, agricultural production and resource conservation.

But actual public expenditures for agriculture and rural development in the developing world do not reflect the importance of the sector to the national economies and the livelihood of their

6

"We will promote optimal allocation and use of public and private investments to foster human resources ... and rural development."

populations. In fact, government expenditures on agriculture come closest to matching the economic importance of the sector in those countries where hunger is least prevalent. For the group of countries where undernourishment is most widespread, the share of government spending devoted to agriculture falls far short of matching the sector's importance in the economy.

The trends are also discouraging. During most of the 1990s, the agricultural orientation index (calculated as the ratio of the share of agriculture in total public expenditures to the share of agriculture in GDP) increased in the countries with the lowest prevalence of undernourishment while decreasing in the countries where the prevalence was highest.

Development assistance does not target neediest countries

Development assistance is critical for very poor countries with limited ability to mobilize domestic private and public savings for investment. It is particularly critical for agriculture, which is largely bypassed by foreign private investors.

And yet official development assistance to agriculture declined by an alarming 48 percent between 1990 and 1999 in real terms.

It also appears that external assistance to agriculture (EAA) is not related to need. Data on EAA for 1997–99 indicate that countries where less than 5 percent of the population was undernourished received more than three times as much assistance per agricultural worker as countries where more than 35 percent of the population was undernourished. Moreover, although EAA per agricultural worker declined across all categories in the 1990s, the countries with the highest prevalence of undernourishment were the hardest hit. In those countries, EAA declined by 49 percent in real terms, leaving it at less than 40 percent of the level per agricultural worker in countries with the lowest prevalence of hunger.

The message is clear. Directing sufficient resources to agriculture and rural development will increase productivity, employment opportunities and access to food, particularly in the rural areas and countries where hunger is most common. Many of these countries are badly starved of investable resources.

International assistance to them, starting with a lasting solution of the debt problem, would be a tangible sign that the commitments to reach the World Food Summit goals are being honoured.

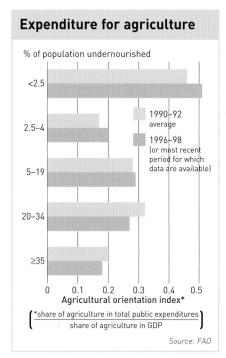

Expenditure for agriculture

% of population undernourished

- 1990–92 average
- 1996–98 (or most recent period for which data are available)

Agricultural orientation index*

$$\left(*\frac{\text{share of agriculture in total public expenditures}}{\text{share of agriculture in GDP}}\right)$$

Source: FAO

Bringing hunger reduction on track – what should it take?

To accelerate progress in reducing hunger and reach the goals of the World Food Summit (WFS), FAO has estimated that additional public investments of some US$24 billion annually are needed in five priority areas. The investments would be focused on poor countries with large numbers of undernourished people.

Coupled with steps to create an enabling policy framework, the additional resources are expected to stimulate private investment and bring about substantial and sustainable reductions in hunger and poverty. The proposal estimates that the benefits of reaching the WFS goal would be at least US$120 billion per year as a result of longer, healthier and more productive lives for several hundred million people.

The proposed package aims at increasing productivity (including through providing food assistance to

people debilitated by hunger), enhancing knowledge and protecting and sustaining the resource base. Financing for the programme would be divided more or less equally between official development assistance and recipient country budgets.

The priority areas and estimated annual investments outlined in the proposal include:

- to raise farm productivity in poor rural communities – US$2.3 billion per year;
- to promote sustainable use of natural resources – US$7.4 billion per year;
- to cover investments in rural infrastructure and market access – US$7.8 billion;
- to support agricultural research and extension and nutrition education – US$1.1 billion;
- to improve direct access to food for the most needy – US$5.2 billion.

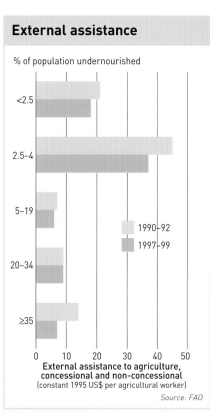

External assistance

% of population undernourished

- 1990–92
- 1997–99

External assistance to agriculture, concessional and non-concessional (constant 1995 US$ per agricultural worker)

Source: FAO

The way ahead

Combating hunger contributes to achieving other Millennium Development Goals

THE LATEST FIGURES AND ANALYSIS presented in this report make it clear that progress in reducing hunger over the 1990s was rapid in just a few countries, painfully slow in others, and non-existent or negative across much of the developing world. If we continue at the present uneven and sluggish pace, the number of hungry people in the developing world in 2015 will still total more than 750 million, far above the goal of around 400 million established at the 1996 World Food Summit (WFS).

But the rest of this report makes it equally clear that the lack of progress does not result from a lack of knowledge about what needs to be done. It is not that we have lost our way but rather that we have not followed it. Last year's report on *The State of Food Insecurity in the World* summed up the way ahead simply and powerfully – "commitment, followed by resources and action". That prescription remains just as valid today.

Slow progress, but some encouraging signs

While evidence of progress remains scarce, the year 2002 has offered several encouraging signs of renewed commitment, expanded resources and more determined action. We have seen evidence of renewed commitment in the growing momentum behind the Millennium Development Goals (MDGs) and in expressions of support for the progressive realization of the right to food at the World Food Summit: *five years later*. We have witnessed pledges of increased resources at the Conference on Financing for Development in Monterrey. And we have seen the outlines of a practical, affordable programme of action take shape in the twin-track approach to combating hunger advanced by FAO, the World Food Programme and the International Fund for Agricultural Development at the Monterrey conference. That twin-track approach was later elaborated by the FAO

Secretariat in the draft proposal for an Anti-Hunger Programme.

The Anti-Hunger Programme is fully consistent with the WFS Plan of Action. Likewise, the halving of hunger and poverty will make an essential contribution to all other MDGs. The Anti-Hunger Programme proposes priority actions and the related resource requirements to accelerate the implementation and amplify the impact of the Summit's Plan of Action.

Accelerating progress

Numerous articles in this report offer compelling evidence that the WFS target and the MDGs are interdependent and mutually reinforcing. Few of the MDGs can be achieved without substantially reducing hunger. By the same token, progress towards the other MDGs will accelerate progress on reducing hunger and poverty.

To cite just one example, MDG Number Three calls for efforts to promote gender equality and empower women. In many impoverished rural areas, food insecurity and poverty sharply reduce school attendance of girls. Similarly, hunger and poverty frequently compel women to devote their energies to subsistence agriculture to feed their families, while men often migrate to cities in search of work. Reducing hunger would open the door to new opportunities for both women and men in rural areas.

At the same time, numerous studies have confirmed that reducing gender inequality and empowering women would yield significant reductions in hunger and poverty. One World Bank study found that increasing women's primary schooling could boost agricultural output by 24 percent. Other studies have shown that increasing opportunities for women has a particularly strong impact on hunger because women devote much more of their income directly to feeding their families than men do.

A similar case can be made for positive

feedback between combating hunger and reaching other MDGs (see box, page 11). The evidence is clear that hunger can lead to unsustainable use of resources and that environmental degradation contributes to hunger; that hunger is a major cause of maternal deaths and that poor maternal nutrition and health perpetuate hunger by increasing the number of children of low birth weight who suffer from impaired cognitive and physical development; that hunger contributes to the spread and lethal impact of HIV/AIDS, malaria and other diseases, while the AIDS pandemic has caused widespread hunger by decimating the agricultural workforce and leaving many rural households struggling to survive on the labour of orphaned children and elderly relatives.

Entering a virtuous cycle

All of these interconnections suggest that the way ahead is a multi-lane highway. To accelerate along it, we must give urgent priority to the fight against hunger, as an essential step toward progress on other fronts. And we must also redouble our efforts to achieve the other MDGs, knowing that progress will yield invaluable gains in reducing hunger and poverty.

By answering the calls for an international alliance against hunger and a global partnership for development, we can escape from the vicious cycle in which hunger and poverty are perpetuated, in part, by the crippling damage they inflict on human lives and natural resources. And we can enter a virtuous cycle, in which every investment in achieving one of our development goals accelerates progress towards reaching them all.

Tables

Table 1. PREVALENCE OF UNDERNOURISHMENT in developing countries and countries in transition

DEVELOPING WORLD Region/subregion/country [undernourishment category]	Total population			Number of people undernourished			Proportion of undernourished in total population		
	1979–81	1990–92 millions	1998–2000	1979–81	1990–92 millions	1998–2000	1979–81	1990–92 %	1998–2000
DEVELOPING WORLD	3 240.2	4 050.0	4 638.9	920.0	818.5	798.8	28	20	17
ASIA AND THE PACIFIC	2 303.5	2 812.1	3 162.5	727.3	567.3	508.1	32	20	16
East Asia	1 060.9	1 241.1	1 342.4	307.7	198.2	128.4	29	16	10
China* [3]	998.9	1 169.5	1 264.6	303.8	193.0	119.1	30	16	9
Dem. People's Rep. of Korea [4]	17.2	20.3	22.1	3.0	3.7	7.5	18	18	34
Hong Kong SAR of China [1]	5.0	5.8	6.7	0.1	0.1	0.1	-	-	-
Mongolia [5]	1.7	2.3	2.5	0.3	0.8	1.0	16	34	42
Rep. of Korea [1]	38.1	43.3	46.4	0.5	0.8	0.7	-	-	-
OCEANIA	3.0	3.9	4.7	0.7	0.9	1.3	24	25	27
Papua New Guinea [4]	3.0	3.9	4.7	0.7	0.9	1.3	24	25	27
SOUTHEAST ASIA	354.8	444.8	509.4	88.4	76.5	63.5	25	17	12
Cambodia [5]	6.7	10.0	12.8	4.0	4.3	4.6	60	43	36
Indonesia [3]	150.3	185.6	209.3	36.6	16.7	12.3	24	9	6
Lao People's Dem. Rep. [4]	3.2	4.2	5.2	1.0	1.2	1.2	33	29	24
Malaysia [1]	13.8	18.3	21.8	0.5	0.6	0.4	4	3	-
Myanmar [3]	33.7	41.3	47.1	6.2	4.0	3.1	18	10	6
Philippines [4]	48.0	62.5	74.2	12.8	16.2	16.8	27	26	23
Thailand [3]	46.0	55.5	62.0	10.4	15.6	11.5	23	28	18
Viet Nam [3]	53.0	67.5	77.1	16.8	18.0	13.7	32	27	18
SOUTH ASIA	884.9	1 122.4	1 306.1	330.5	291.6	314.9	37	26	24
Bangladesh [5]	85.5	112.7	134.6	33.8	39.2	47.0	40	35	35
India [4]	689.0	861.3	992.7	261.5	215.6	233.3	38	25	24
Nepal [3]	14.6	18.6	22.5	7.1	3.5	4.3	49	19	19
Pakistan [3]	81.3	112.5	137.6	25.1	28.2	26.0	31	25	19
Sri Lanka [4]	14.6	17.2	18.7	3.0	5.0	4.3	21	29	23
LATIN AMERICA AND THE CARIBBEAN	355.9	442.2	504.4	45.9	58.8	54.8	13	13	11
NORTH AMERICA	67.6	84.8	97.4	3.0	4.3	5.2	4	5	5
Mexico [3]	67.6	84.8	97.4	3.0	4.3	5.2	4	5	5
CENTRAL AMERICA	22.1	28.7	35.2	4.5	4.8	7.1	20	17	20
Costa Rica [3]	2.3	3.1	3.9	0.2	0.2	0.2	8	6	5
El Salvador [3]	4.6	5.2	6.2	0.8	0.6	0.8	17	12	14
Guatemala [4]	6.8	9.0	11.1	1.2	1.2	2.8	18	14	25
Honduras [4]	3.6	5.0	6.3	1.1	1.1	1.3	31	23	21
Nicaragua [4]	2.9	3.9	4.9	0.8	1.2	1.5	26	30	29
Panama [3]	1.9	2.4	2.8	0.4	0.5	0.5	21	19	18
THE CARIBBEAN	24.1	28.5	31.3	4.7	7.4	7.9	20	26	25
Cuba [3]	9.7	10.7	11.2	0.4	0.5	1.5	4	5	13
Dominican Rep. [4]	5.7	7.2	8.2	1.4	1.9	2.1	25	27	26
Haiti [5]	5.5	7.0	8.0	2.6	4.5	4.0	48	64	50
Jamaica [3]	2.1	2.4	2.6	0.2	0.3	0.2	10	14	9
Trinidad and Tobago [3]	1.1	1.2	1.3	0.1	0.2	0.2	6	13	12
SOUTH AMERICA	242.2	300.1	340.6	33.8	42.3	34.6	14	14	10
Argentina [1]	28.1	33.0	36.6	0.3	0.7	0.4	-	-	-
Bolivia [4]	5.4	6.7	8.1	1.4	1.7	1.9	26	26	23
Brazil [3]	121.6	150.3	168.2	18.1	19.4	16.7	15	13	10
Chile [2]	11.1	13.3	15.0	0.7	1.1	0.6	7	8	4
Colombia [3]	28.4	35.7	41.4	6.1	6.1	5.6	22	17	13
Ecuador [3]	8.0	10.5	12.4	0.9	0.9	0.7	11	8	5
Guyana [3]	0.8	0.7	0.8	0.1	0.1	0.1	13	19	14
Paraguay [3]	3.1	4.3	5.4	0.4	0.8	0.7	13	18	14
Peru [3]	17.3	22.0	25.2	4.9	8.9	2.9	28	40	11
Suriname [3]	0.4	0.4	0.4	0.1	0.0	0.0	18	12	11
Uruguay [2]	2.9	3.1	3.3	0.1	0.2	0.1	3	6	3
Venezuela [4]	15.1	20.0	23.7	0.6	2.3	4.9	4	11	21

Tables

Table 1 cont. PREVALENCE OF UNDERNOURISHMENT in developing countries and countries in transition

DEVELOPING WORLD Region/subregion/country [undernourishment category]	Total population			Number of people undernourished			Proportion of undernourished in total population		
	1979–81	1990–92 millions	1998–2000	1979–81	1990–92 millions	1998–2000	1979–81	1990–92 %	1998–2000
NEAR EAST AND NORTH AFRICA	237.0	321.3	384.5	21.5	26.0	40.0	9	8	10
NEAR EAST	145.6	200.6	244.2	14.1	20.5	33.8	10	10	14
Afghanistan [5]	15.0	14.6	21.2	5.6	9.2	14.9	37	63	70
Iran, Islamic Rep. [3]	39.2	59.9	69.2	2.6	2.7	3.8	7	4	5
Iraq [4]	13.0	17.8	22.3	0.5	1.2	5.9	4	7	27
Jordan [3]	2.2	3.4	4.8	0.1	0.1	0.3	6	4	6
Kuwait [2]	1.4	2.1	1.8	0.1	0.5	0.1	4	22	4
Lebanon [2]	2.7	2.8	3.4	0.2	0.1	0.1	8	-	3
Saudi Arabia [2]	9.6	15.8	19.6	0.3	0.6	0.6	3	4	3
Syrian Arab Rep. [2]	8.7	12.8	15.8	0.3	0.6	0.5	3	5	3
Turkey [1]	44.7	57.2	65.7	1.2	1.0	1.6	3	-	-
United Arab Emirates [1]	1.0	2.1	2.6	0.0	0.1	0.1	-	3	-
Yemen [4]	8.2	12.2	17.6	3.2	4.4	5.9	39	36	33
NORTH AFRICA	91.4	120.7	140.3	7.4	5.5	6.2	8	5	4
Algeria [3]	18.7	25.4	29.8	1.7	1.3	1.7	9	5	6
Egypt [2]	43.8	57.4	66.7	3.6	2.6	2.5	8	5	4
Libyan Arab Jamahiriya [1]	3.0	4.4	5.2	0.0	0.0	0.0	-	-	-
Morocco [3]	19.4	25.1	29.3	1.9	1.5	2.0	10	6	7
Tunisia [1]	6.4	8.3	9.4	0.2	0.1	0.0	3	-	-
SUB-SAHARAN AFRICA	343.8	474.5	587.5	125.4	166.4	195.9	36	35	33
CENTRAL AFRICA	44.8	62.8	79.6	15.1	22.0	45.1	34	35	57
Cameroon [4]	8.7	11.9	14.6	2.0	3.8	3.6	22	32	25
Central African Rep. [5]	2.3	3.0	3.6	0.6	1.5	1.6	24	49	44
Chad [4]	4.5	6.0	7.6	3.1	3.5	2.5	68	58	32
Congo [4]	1.7	2.3	2.9	0.5	0.9	0.9	31	37	32
Dem. Rep. of the Congo [5]	26.9	38.5	49.6	8.9	12.3	36.4	33	32	73
Gabon [3]	0.7	1.0	1.2	0.1	0.1	0.1	13	11	8
EAST AFRICA	120.4	166.1	204.0	42.5	73.7	83.0	35	44	41
Burundi [5]	4.1	5.7	6.3	1.6	2.8	4.3	39	49	69
Eritrea [5]	na	na	3.5	na	na	2.0	na	na	58
Ethiopia [5]	na	na	61.4	na	na	27.1	na	na	44
Kenya [5]	16.4	24.3	30.0	4.0	11.5	13.2	24	47	44
Rwanda [5]	5.2	6.4	7.0	1.2	2.2	2.8	24	34	40
Somalia [5]	6.4	7.2	8.4	4.3	4.8	6.0	67	67	71
Sudan [4]	19.3	25.4	30.4	5.6	7.8	6.5	29	31	21
Uganda [4]	12.5	17.8	22.6	4.1	4.1	4.7	33	23	21
United Rep. of Tanzania [5]	18.8	27.0	34.3	5.2	9.8	16.2	28	36	47
SOUTHERN AFRICA	51.9	71.0	87.1	17.0	34.0	37.1	33	48	43
Angola [5]	7.1	9.9	12.8	2.6	6.0	6.3	37	61	50
Botswana [4]	0.9	1.3	1.5	0.3	0.2	0.4	30	17	25
Lesotho [4]	1.4	1.7	2.0	0.4	0.5	0.5	30	27	26
Madagascar [5]	9.1	12.3	15.5	1.8	4.3	6.2	20	35	40
Malawi [4]	6.2	9.6	11.0	1.6	4.8	3.7	26	49	33
Mauritius [3]	1.0	1.1	1.2	0.1	0.1	0.1	10	6	5
Mozambique [5]	11.8	14.1	17.9	6.5	9.7	9.8	55	69	55
Namibia [3]	1.0	1.4	1.7	0.2	0.2	0.2	20	15	9
Swaziland [3]	0.6	0.8	0.9	0.1	0.1	0.1	14	10	12
Zambia [5]	5.9	8.3	10.2	1.5	3.7	5.1	26	45	50
Zimbabwe [5]	7.1	10.5	12.4	1.9	4.5	4.7	26	43	38
WEST AFRICA	126.7	174.7	216.7	50.7	36.7	30.7	40	21	14
Benin [3]	3.5	4.8	6.1	1.3	0.9	0.8	37	19	13
Burkina Faso [4]	6.9	9.3	11.3	4.5	2.2	2.6	64	23	23
Côte d'Ivoire [3]	8.5	13.0	15.7	0.7	2.3	2.3	8	18	15
Gambia [4]	0.6	1.0	1.3	0.4	0.2	0.3	58	21	21
Ghana [3]	11.0	15.6	18.9	7.1	5.5	2.2	64	35	12
Guinea [4]	4.7	6.4	8.0	1.5	2.5	2.6	32	40	32

Table 1 *cont.* PREVALENCE OF UNDERNOURISHMENT in developing countries and countries in transition

DEVELOPING WORLD Region/subregion/country [undernourishment category]	Total population			Number of people undernourished			Proportion of undernourished in total population		
	1979–81	1990–92 millions	1998–2000	1979–81	1990–92 millions	1998–2000	1979–81	1990–92 %	1998–2000
Liberia [5]	1.9	2.1	2.7	0.4	0.7	1.0	22	33	39
Mali [4]	6.8	9.0	11.0	4.1	2.2	2.3	60	25	20
Mauritania [3]	1.6	2.0	2.6	0.5	0.3	0.3	35	14	12
Niger [5]	5.6	8.0	10.5	1.9	3.3	3.8	34	42	36
Nigeria [3]	64.3	88.5	110.9	25.2	11.9	7.3	39	13	7
Senegal [4]	5.5	7.5	9.2	1.3	1.7	2.3	23	23	25
Sierra Leone [5]	3.2	4.1	4.3	1.3	1.9	2.0	40	46	47
Togo [4]	2.5	3.5	4.4	0.7	1.0	1.0	26	28	23

COUNTRIES IN TRANSITION Region/subregion/country [undernourishment category]	Total population 1998–2000 millions	Number of people undernourished 1998–2000 millions	Proportion of undernourished in total population 1998–2000 %
COUNTRIES IN TRANSITION	**412.6**	**30.2**	**7**
COMMONWEALTH OF INDEPENDENT STATES	284.0	25.5	9
Armenia [5]	3.8	1.8	46
Azerbaijan [4]	8.0	1.9	23
Belarus [1]	10.2	0.2	-
Georgia [3]	5.3	0.9	16
Kazakhstan [3]	16.3	1.2	8
Kyrgyzstan [3]	4.8	0.4	8
Rep. of Moldova [3]	4.3	0.4	10
Russian Fed. [3]	146.2	7.2	5
Tajikistan [5]	6.0	3.9	64
Turkmenistan [3]	4.6	0.4	8
Ukraine [3]	50.0	2.6	5
Uzbekistan [3]	24.5	4.7	19
BALTIC STATES	7.5	0.3	3
Estonia [1]	1.4	0.0	-
Latvia [3]	2.4	0.1	5
Lithuania [2]	3.7	0.1	3
EASTERN EUROPE	121.0	4.5	4
Albania [3]	3.1	0.3	8
Bosnia and Herzegovina [3]	3.8	0.2	6
Bulgaria [3]	8.0	1.2	15
Croatia [3]	4.7	0.8	18
Czech Rep. [1]	10.3	0.2	-
Hungary [1]	10.0	0.1	-
TFYR Macedonia [2]	2.0	0.1	4
Poland [1]	38.6	0.3	-
Romania [1]	22.5	0.3	-
Slovakia [1]	5.4	0.1	-
Slovenia [1]	2.0	0.0	-
Yugoslavia, Fed. Rep. of ** [3]	10.6	0.8	8

NOTES:
Figures following country name refer to the prevalence categories (proportion of the population undernourished in 1998-2000):
[1]   <2.5% undernourished
[2]   2.5–4% undernourished
[3]   5–19% undernourished
[4]   20–34% undernourished
[5]   ≥35% undernourished

KEY:
na   not available
–   proportion less than 2.5% undernourished
*   includes Taiwan Province of China
**   Serbia and Montenegro
Table does not include countries for which there were insufficient data
SOURCES: Total population: *UN Population Prospects*, 2000 revision
                Undernourishment: FAO estimates

Tables

Table 2. FOOD AVAILABILITY, DIET DIVERSIFICATION, POVERTY, HEALTH , CHILD NUTRITIONAL STATUS in developing countries and countries in transition, classified by category of prevalence of undernourishment

CATEGORY OF PREVALENCE of undernourishment in total population 1998–2000; region and country	FOOD AVAILABILITY AND DIET DIVERSIFICATION		POVERTY	HEALTH		CHILD NUTRITIONAL STATUS
	Dietary energy supply (DES) 1998–2000	Share of non-starchy food in total DES	People living on less than US$1 per day 1990s (last survey)	Life expectancy at birth 2000	Under-five mortality rate 2000	Underweight children under five years of age 1990–2000 (last survey)
	kcal/day per person	%	%	years	per 1 000 births	%
LESS THAN 2.5% UNDERNOURISHED						
ASIA AND THE PACIFIC						
Hong Kong SAR of China	3 100	70	na	80	na	na
Malaysia	2 930	56	na	73	9	18
Rep. of Korea	3 060	49	-	73	5	na
LATIN AMERICA AND THE CARIBBEAN						
Argentina	3 180	66	na	74	21	na
NEAR EAST AND NORTH AFRICA						
Libyan Arab Jamahiriya	3 300	53	na	71	20	5
Tunisia	3 360	48	-	72	28	4
Turkey	3 390	47	2	70	45	8
United Arab Emirates	3 180	65	na	75	9	14
COUNTRIES IN TRANSITION						
Belarus	3 050	53	-	68	20	na
Czech Rep.	3 170	69	-	75	5	1
Estonia	3 250	53	-	71	21	na
Hungary	3 420	70	-	71	9	na
Poland	3 370	58	-	73	10	na
Romania	3 280	47	3	70	22	6
Slovakia	3 100	65	-	73	9	na
Slovenia	3 080	61	-	75	5	na
2.5 TO 4% UNDERNOURISHED						
LATIN AMERICA AND THE CARIBBEAN						
Chile	2 850	57	-	76	12	1
Uruguay	2 850	63	-	74	17	5
NEAR EAST AND NORTH AFRICA						
Egypt	3 320	34	3	67	43	12
Kuwait	3 130	62	na	77	10	10
Lebanon	3 160	62	na	70	32	3
Saudi Arabia	2 840	51	na	73	29	14
Syrian Arab Rep.	3 050	52	na	70	29	13
COUNTRIES IN TRANSITION						
Lithuania	3 010	47	-	73	21	na
TFYR of Macedonia	2 960	58	na	73	26	6
5 TO 19% UNDERNOURISHED						
ASIA AND THE PACIFIC						
China*	3 030	39	19	70	40	10
Indonesia	2 900	29	8	66	48	26
Myanmar	2 820	24	na	56	110	36
Nepal	2 380	21	38	59	100	47
Pakistan	2 460	47	31	63	110	38
Thailand	2 480	49	-	69	29	19
Viet Nam	2 540	26	na	69	39	33
LATIN AMERICA AND THE CARIBBEAN						
Brazil	2 960	65	12	68	38	6
Colombia	2 570	60	20	72	30	7
Costa Rica	2 780	62	13	77	12	5
Cuba	2 560	60	na	76	9	4
Ecuador	2 680	62	20	70	32	15
El Salvador	2 460	46	21	70	40	12
Guyana	2 550	48	na	63	74	12

KEY: * includes Taiwan Province of China for FAO estimates; ** Serbia and Montenegro; na not available; – proportion less than 2%.

Table 2 cont. FOOD AVAILABILITY, DIET DIVERSIFICATION, POVERTY, HEALTH, CHILD NUTRITIONAL STATUS in developing countries and countries in transition, classified by category of prevalence of undernourishment

CATEGORY OF PREVALENCE of undernourishment in total population 1998–2000; region and country	FOOD AVAILABILITY AND DIET DIVERSIFICATION		POVERTY	HEALTH		CHILD NUTRITIONAL STATUS
	Dietary energy supply (DES) 1998–2000	Share of non-starchy food in total DES 1998–2000	People living on less than US$1 per day 1990s (last survey)	Life expectancy at birth 2000	Under-five mortality rate 2000	Underweight children under five years of age 1990–2000 (last survey)
	kcal/day per person	%	%	years	per 1 000 births	%
Jamaica	2 680	59	3	75	20	4
Mexico	3 150	53	16	73	30	8
Panama	2 410	62	14	75	26	7
Paraguay	2 540	57	20	70	31	5
Peru	2 600	46	16	69	50	8
Suriname	2 630	57	na	70	33	na
Trinidad and Tobago	2 720	61	12	73	20	na
NEAR EAST AND NORTH AFRICA						
Algeria	2 960	39	-	71	65	6
Iran, Islamic Rep. of	2 910	39	na	69	44	11
Jordan	2 720	47	-	72	34	5
Morocco	3 010	36	-	67	46	9
SUB-SAHARAN AFRICA						
Benin	2 570	26	na	53	154	29
Côte d'Ivoire	2 590	33	12	46	173	21
Gabon	2 550	55	na	53	90	na
Ghana	2 650	28	45	57	102	25
Mauritania	2 660	45	29	52	183	23
Mauritius	2 970	54	na	72	20	16
Namibia	2 600	27	35	47	69	26
Nigeria	2 840	35	70	47	184	27
Swaziland	2 570	52	na	46	142	na
COUNTRIES IN TRANSITION						
Albania	2 750	52	na	74	31	14
Bosnia and Herzegovina	2 810	42	na	73	18	4
Bulgaria	2 640	63	-	72	16	na
Croatia	2 480	62	-	73	9	1
Georgia	2 440	38	-	73	29	3
Kazakhstan	2 720	41	-	65	75	4
Kyrgyzstan	2 830	34	na	67	63	11
Latvia	2 880	58	-	70	21	na
Rep. of Moldova	2 730	48	11	68	33	3
Russian Fed.	2 900	52	7	65	22	3
Turkmenistan	2 720	37	12	66	70	na
Ukraine	2 830	49	3	68	21	3
Uzbekistan	2 370	42	3	70	67	19
Yugoslavia, Fed. Rep. of **	2 750	68	na	72	20	2
20 TO 34% UNDERNOURISHED						
ASIA AND THE PACIFIC						
Dem. People's Rep. of Korea	2 170	32	na	61	30	60
India	2 430	38	44	63	96	47
Lao People's Dem. Rep.	2 240	21	26	54	105	40
Papua New Guinea	2 180	44	na	59	112	na
Philippines	2 360	44	na	69	40	28
Sri Lanka	2 360	44	7	73	19	33
LATIN AMERICA AND THE CARIBBEAN						
Bolivia	2 210	51	14	63	80	10
Dominican Rep.	2 310	67	3	67	48	5
Guatemala	2 160	47	10	65	59	24
Honduras	2 390	54	24	66	40	25
Nicaragua	2 240	49	na	69	45	12

NOTES: The underweight refers to children below five years of age (0–59 months), except: 0–35 months Benin, Eritrea, India, Kyrgyzstan, Mozambique, Nigeria, Togo and Uzbekistan; 0–71 months Chile, Congo, and Costa Rica; 6–59 months Dem. People's Rep. of Korea, Nepal and TFYR Macedonia; 3–35 months Bolivia and Mali; 12–71 months Croatia and Honduras; 3–59 months El Salvador and Guatemala; 6–35 months Afghanistan; 0–72 months China; 0–36 months Côte d'Ivoire; 0–48 months Guyana; 0–47 months Uganda.

Tables

Table 2 cont. FOOD AVAILABILITY, DIET DIVERSIFICATION, POVERTY, HEALTH, CHILD NUTRITIONAL STATUS in developing countries and countries in transition, classified by category of prevalence of undernourishment						
CATEGORY OF PREVALENCE of undernourishment in total population 1998–2000; region and country	FOOD AVAILABILITY AND DIET DIVERSIFICATION		POVERTY	HEALTH		CHILD NUTRITIONAL STATUS
	Dietary energy supply (DES)	Share of non-starchy food in total DES	People living on less than US$1 per day 1990s (last survey)	Life expectancy at birth	Under-five mortality rate	Underweight children under five years of age 1990–2000 (last survey)
	1998–2000			2000		
	kcal/day per person	%	%	years	per 1 000 births	%
Venezuela	2 280	60	23	73	23	5
NEAR EAST AND NORTH AFRICA						
Iraq	2 150	34	na	61	130	16
Yemen	2 040	33	16	56	117	46
SUB-SAHARAN AFRICA						
Botswana	2 240	50	na	39	101	13
Burkina Faso	2 320	25	61	44	198	34
Cameroon	2 270	41	33	50	154	21
Chad	2 180	40	na	48	198	28
Congo	2 170	36	na	51	108	14
Gambia	2 400	45	59	53	128	17
Guinea	2 240	41	na	46	175	23
Lesotho	2 300	19	43	44	133	16
Malawi	2 160	24	na	39	188	25
Mali	2 400	28	73	42	233	43
Senegal	2 260	40	26	52	139	18
Sudan	2 360	43	na	56	108	17
Togo	2 370	21	na	49	142	25
Uganda	2 330	56	na	42	127	26
COUNTRIES IN TRANSITION						
Azerbaijan	2 330	33	-	72	105	17
35% OR MORE UNDERNOURISHED						
ASIA AND THE PACIFIC						
Bangladesh	2 100	16	29	61	82	48
Cambodia	1 990	22	na	54	135	46
Mongolia	2 020	56	14	67	78	13
LATIN AMERICA AND THE CARIBBEAN						
Haiti	2 040	46	na	53	125	28
NEAR EAST AND NORTH AFRICA						
Afghanistan	1 630	27	na	43	257	48
SUB-SAHARAN AFRICA						
Angola	1 890	33	na	47	295	na
Burundi	1 620	51	na	42	190	45
Central African Rep.	1 950	44	67	43	180	24
Dem. Rep. of the Congo	1 590	23	na	46	207	34
Eritrea	1 710	22	na	52	114	44
Ethiopia	1 880	19	31	42	174	47
Kenya	1 960	41	27	47	120	23
Liberia	2 140	38	na	47	235	na
Madagascar	2 010	25	49	55	139	33
Mozambique	1 910	23	38	42	200	26
Niger	2 100	28	61	46	270	40
Rwanda	2 020	52	na	40	187	29
Sierra Leone	1 980	36	57	39	316	27
Somalia	1 600	65	na	48	225	26
United Rep. of Tanzania	1 920	30	20	44	165	29
Zambia	1 900	21	64	38	202	25
Zimbabwe	2 110	38	36	40	117	13
COUNTRIES IN TRANSITION						
Armenia	2 040	36	8	74	30	3
Tajikistan	1 790	31	na	69	73	na

SOURCES: Dietary energy supply (DES) and share of non-starchy food: FAO estimates; Poverty: *World Development Indicators 2002*, World Bank; Life expectancy at birth: World Development Indicators online database, World Bank, July 2002; Under-five mortality and child nutritional status: UNICEF online database, Sept. 2001.